In August 1994, Alfredo Jaar went to Rwanda to see with his own eyes what had happened there. There he was faced with an absolute genocide: millions of people killed, wounded or disappeared. Two ethnic groups, Hutus and Tutsis, locked in a battle to the death, in a society ravaged by poverty, disease and hunger.
That trip culminated, in the year 2000, in one of his most important and meaningful works, a piece that today forms part of the MUSAC collection: *Emergencia*. A black pool, out of which, at regular intervals, the African continent heaves itself up like a Leviathan. If his work has always explored and denounced limit situations of exploitation, immigration, exile and illegality, the brutality of the Rwandan genocide led Alfredo Jaar to undertake a more scientific work, setting out to understand the vision the world forms of realities through the images available to it.
In the light of the importance of this work, the Government of the Autonomous Region of Castille and Leon is inaugurating the Museum of Contemporary Art of Castille and Leon (MUSAC) with an exhibition entitled *Emergencias*. This exhibition, in which the work of Alfredo Jaar has a special importance, sets out to highlight the role played by artists and their work in interpreting the events that accompany our daily lives.
Approximately five years ago, the BildMuseet in Sweden published, to accompany the exhibiting of this piece, a book with the same name, *Emergency*. In this publication, eighteen African writers, whose roots lie in this forgotten continent, narrated their dreams, their desires and their hopes for the land that produced them.
Today MUSAC adds its weight to this project by publishing an extended version of this book, which includes 7 new essays, thereby offering an overall vision of what is going on around us. Whilst marking the inauguration of this new artistic space, the project also sets out to illustrate the commitment of contemporary art to our society.

Silvia Clemente Municio
Councillor for Culture and Tourism

Emergency

This book is both a fragment of, and an extension to, the work "Emergency" (1998) by Alfredo Jaar. It takes the form of a collection of texts in which twenty-five African writers reflect on what Africa is, and what it means for them at this time. Each text has a different focus, each author a distinct posture, echoing in this way the diversity that is implicit in the continent itself. Doubtless, as a form of reflection this is, *a priori*, a risky exercise and one which is made more difficult by the complexity inherent in African geography. Alfredo Jaar, rather than offering his own theories about the continent, has chosen instead to step back and leave the stage to those he considers more qualified to express an opinion about the state of Africa. His piece acts as an axis around which a wide range of reflections are generated. These in turn enrich the unitary discourse of the original piece, the individual signature of the creator that every work of art bears. Despite the plurality of postures adopted by the participating authors, all of their texts, even the most optimistic and utopian of them, highlight the necessity, or rather the urgency (emergency) of confronting the problems that still bind the continent in a situation of physical and psychological poverty.

The artist's original idea was to publish the book in parallel to the displaying of his work in the Swedish BildMuseet in the year 2000. At that time, eighteen writers were invited to participate in the project and the resulting book was published in Swedish. Four years later, with the piece having been acquired by MUSAC as one of the central pillars around which to build its collection, a commitment was made to republish it. At Alfredo Jaar's suggestion, the publication has now been extended with the addition of seven new essays that respond to the same question the artist posed some years ago, thereby strengthening even further the links with the present. Unfortunately, the problems described are just as real, if not more so, now. Thus, the texts written four or five years ago remain as valid today as they were then, and the questions they

raise continue to be left hanging in the air, like suggestions waiting for interlocutors willing to listen to them.
Similarly, the piece "Emergency", the starting point for this publication, has also led to the creation of a wide-ranging project the results of which are shown in MUSAC's first exhibition. The title of the project is *Emergencies*. Going beyond the simple presentation of an accumulation of the most recent artistic creations, this project sets out to analyse, using the museum's own collection, the social and political position adopted in the art produced in our times.

"Emergency", the work by Alfredo Jaar with which this museum of the 21st century is to be inaugurated, aims to be a direct and raw illustration of one of the most serious conflicts humanity faces in this century, a conflict to which it is urgent to find a realistic and committed response. Africa, as a great question mark, as a great but moribund wild beast, as a great treasure squandered and vilified, as the antithesis of modernity, as the unforgettable nightmare, as the finger of blame that points accusingly at the rest of the world, as the blinding vision to be avoided at all costs, as the broken dream of some distant god, as the wreckage of a sunken ship...; but also as the seed of hope, as the last bastion of the human soul, as the territory that yearns for the utopia that is yet to arrive..., and above all else, as A PLACE THAT IS POSSIBLE.

Rafael Doctor Roncero
Director of MUSAC

Abdourahman Waberi

The endless vitality of Africa

Let's begin by recalling an event that had fatal consequences: Yaguine Koita (fourteen) and Fodé Tounkara (fifteen), two boys from Guinea, were found dead in the undercarriage of a Sabena airliner when it arrived in Brussels. The Belgian police found a letter that the two teenagers had written on 21 July 1999, that is, two days before stowing away in Conakry. In the letter the boys addressed the leaders of the world ("to the distinguished heads of Europe") to explain their deplorable situation, excusing themselves in advance for their importunity ("we are suffering a lot in Africa [and we would ask] your forgiveness for writing to you"). The entire world was shocked, and television screens all over the planet showed a succession of images that highlighted Africa's desperation. In twenty years the face of the continent has changed drastically. In my particular case, I am very clear that, despite living in exile, I belong to the so-called "Afriques Indociles" (to take the title coined by the Cameroon historian Achille Mbembe), that is, to those millions of keen young students, thirsting for knowledge, on whose fragile shoulders lay the hopes for a triumphant future. After independence, with their heads stuffed full of the ardent promises of the apostles of Pan-Africanism such as Kwame Nkrumah, Julius Nyerere, George Padmore or Cheikh Anta Diop, these young men flocked to the universities that were beginning to spring up in Accra, Ibadan, Abidjan, Kampala or Dar Es Salaam. Two decades later, the best of them had taken up leading positions in the universities of their countries prior to joining the brain-drain, tempted by the North-American intellectual institutions and following in the footsteps of figures such as Ali Mazrui, Kwame Anthony Appiah, Manthia Diawara, Okwui Enwezor or Y. V. Mudimbe. The Founding Fathers intoned the hymn of unification in Addis Ababa. But that was yesterday. Now that is just a pleasant warm memory that has been dignified by the passing of time. Independence cha cha, the most widely-heard song back then, is our Proustian madeleine. I am talking about before Biafra and before Rwanda. Independence, the birth of the African nations, military parades, national anthems, the tears and the joys of childbirth, hands held high, raised fists, flags, the iconic liberators (Nkrumah, Kenyatta, Nyerere, Sekou Touré, Holden, Agostino Neto, Burguiba, Nasser, Sisulu, Mandela, etc.), images of the martyrs (Lumumba, Cabral, Biko, Hani...), the omniscient Fathers of the Homeland, the departure of the colonisers, the victory of the guerrillas, anonymous multitudes on the grand days..., the historical movement which had been set in motion seemed unstoppable. The writers, so long prohibited from doing so, took up their pens. Some of them took up positions at the head of the procession to guide the people with their inflamed rhetoric. Baptisms and benedictions. The reclaiming and illustration of past times. The resuscitation of Soundjata, Samory and Chaka. The polishing up of totems of our identity like the Emir Abdelkader, King Béhanzin, Yugurta or André Matsoua. However, on both the political and the economic fronts, things were starting to go wrong. We were driven crazy by the grandness reflected in the barely viable white projects, those projects that we still haven't finished paying for. We became drunk on speeches that first paralysed us and then bred violence and hate.

The 1990s. The image that created the greatest impact during this decade is that of the liberation of Nelson Mandela; the bloodiest, that of the genocide in Rwanda; the most shameful, that of the activist and writer Saro-Wiwa and his eight companions swinging at the end of a rope in a prison in Nigeria, at that time under the iron fist of Sani Abacha, one 10 November in 1995.

But there were grounds for hope, there were reasons to be excited when ten writers, two film-makers and an artist, all Africans, determined to break the silence surrounding the genocide in Rwanda. Armed only with their conviction and their pens, they decided, after the genocide of 1999, to live and reflect for two months in Rwanda "to write, out of the duty to record"[1]. The objective, as Nocky Djedanoum, writer and co-ordinator of the project reminds us, is "to show our solidarity with the people of Rwanda, to try to understand the causes of the genocide and to create works of fiction that will help to preserve the memory of this African tragedy". Many of us were very excited by the possibility that a project as stretching as this might be the first link in a long chain of actions in favour of culture and peace in Africa. While it is true that the main task of the artist, and a difficult one at that, is to put words to a tragedy of such magnitude, another responsibility is that of playing an active role with respect to the future, if only because at the time, culture and intellectuals were mobilised by the autocrats on a massive scale in order to meticulously prepare the genocide.

Finally, there is another reason to be optimistic: the increasingly important role played by women –"the heads with plaits" as Amadou Hampaté Bâ maliciously wrote– in the running of public affairs. As of today, no woman has yet presided over the affairs of an African state, though it is true that there have been advances, even if desperately slow. Obviously, Africa herself, the only one who is capable of expressing herself before the world and of making herself accepted just as she is, still has a long way to go. Instead of stuffing our children with illusions, we should give them security. For in the end, our two young boys from Guinea share the fate of the thousands of Moroccans, and of Africans in general, who week by week risk their lives by crossing the Straits of Gibraltar in an attempt to reach this glittering Europe of abundance, which is so near.

1 Out of this project have come eight published works of fiction, including my *Moisson de crânes* (Le Serpent à plumes, Paris, 2000).

Achmat Dangor

Africa my beginning, Africa my end

"Africa my beginning, Africa my end" are the opening lines from a poem by the late Ingoapele Mandingoane, the South African poet whose fusion of Leopold Senghor's lyricism with harsh, rap-artist rhythms in the 1970 and 1980's presaged the *Kwaito* music so popular among South Africa's youth today. This poem, grandiosely rhetorical in the fashion of medieval troubadours, was both a politcal and a poetic statement. Whether or not we agreed with Mandingoane's politics, or the exclusionist message inherent in this, his most famous poem, we could not but help identify with his powerful urging to throw off the mental shackles that the white man –meaning the colonialists, their physical heirs and the black pretenders who succeeded them in many post-colonial administrations– had imposed on us. We were the generation living in that political twilight between the hey-day of the congress movements and the equally defining advent of the 1976 uprisings.

The Apartheid beast, aided and abetted by (at best) passive Western powers, plodded dumbly towards its Bethlehem for the "rough birth" of separate developement (the misshapen progeny that sought to separate races not only geographically, but mentally as well). Its hob-nailed machine swept aside all overt opposition and relentlessly sniffed out the remnants of clandestine cells that the African Nationalist and Pan African Congresses had set up. Our liberation movements were in exiled disarray, and the leaders left behind had become puny in their accommodating pragmatism. Elsewhere in Africa, the neo-colonialist nightmare was just becoming apparent (how quickly we seemed to go from Kwame Nkruma to Idi Amin, how quickly our own African elite succumbed to the *waBenzi* culture of corrupt indulgence).

At that time, for someone to declare himself African, in the physical and philosophical sense, to announce with fierce optimism that Africa "will arise", required both courage and acute vision. For a while poetry, the ability to articulate the agonies of ordinary people, to turn their lament into clarion calls to the consciences of despots and dictators was the only form of resistance open to us. It may seem like a futile and romantic

way of fighting the south African State for example, which had come to embody the "heart of darkness". But they feared poets and artist, the way ancient tyrants feared soothsayers and magicians. They silenced us with banning orders, detention without trial, murder even.
Today conditions have changed, but the imperatives have not. The poverty, the cultural deprivation the ease with which we adopt not the best attributes of Western (European and North American) culture but its worst, is still there. And we still have only poetry to offer as resistance and as alternatives to the equally remorseless process of "globalisation". Poets are still being killed. Perhaps it is because our words linger in the minds of the few who grow richer while the poor get poorer, it spoils the enjoyment of those among us who live off the crumbs from the globally wealthy, it hangs in the air –a subtle stench– and keeps the uncaring from slipping into their gentle siestas.
So, let me declare: I am an African, and a poet. I make this declaration not so much in salutation to Ingoapele Madingoane but what he stood for: the ability to differ, to do so vehemently, without having to resort to extremes of intolerance. Perhaps he would have questioned my right to call myself African, perhaps not. Yes, he had very firm ideas about what consituted an African, understandably influenced by the hideous racial caste system that Apartheid had fashioned for us: Whites were the Brahmins, Coloured and "Indians" the intermediary merchant and artisan classes, "Black Africans" the untouchables. The degree of our statutory suffering determined the level of our "African-ness" (Ingoapele had to carry a "Passbook", was liable for immediate arrest without it, I was spared this black, plastic covered Star of David).
I would have welcomed a debate with Ingoapele Madingoane. It would have been rich with rhetoric, music, expressive gestures and sways of his dread-locked hair. You see, Africa is a continent of debaters, fierce argument is a ritual as old as the world. The difference now is that we have learned the modern, technological method of resolving our differences: long range cannons, missiles, jet fighters, the AK 47. There was a time when we would have used words, music sometimes, drums

and dancing feet. Have you seen the Zulú or the Moscotho dance not only as warriors but also as messengers and communicators? Have you seen the almost clinical grace with which the *Kaapse Klopse* (Cape Town's street troupes) greet the New Year? Africans always have a story to tell, a parable that will explain life, decipher complex issues, help to bridge ethnic chasms. Our weapons were cultural, designed to absorb the heat of arguments, defuse the potential for violence.

Romantic, archaic, outdated? Well, it can't be worse than the solutions provided by the armies that bestride Africa today, gigantic, decaying forces of "protective" malevolence that consumes budgets, maim sibilinas, and scorch the earth. And it fits so perfectly into what is glibly called the "global economy". Where do these "armed forces" (what a seductive, unthreatening term!) get their arms from, and who benefits and on what scale? Africa has become the consumer of deadly commodities, weapons of war so sophisticated that even children have been given the capacity to commit genocide. Ask the sahreholders of armaments manufacturers to consider the havoc that they are wreaking on the continent, and you will hear bleated denlas, in between the many courses of their sumptuous meals. The new world economic order has established a whole class of exploitative Pontius Pilates, able to wash their hands in the innocence of "share holder" wealth. Weapons of war, like tobacco destroys people's health, why is one a target of the West's moral wrath and the other not?

But today, because Ingoapele is no longer here, I have to qualify my declaration: I am an African, not in the racial, linguistic or even cultural sense. Firstly, because my African-ness is deeply personal affinity with a continent that was my beginning and will probably be my end. Secondly, I must avoid reducing this debate to one about group or tribe, language or race. Like any good debater. I of course need to establish the basis for this philosophical and practical solitariness. I suppose there is something Quixotic in this individual assertion of loyalty to a continent that today lives or dies (at times literally) by collective identity.

There is a story I need to tell, the illustrative parable in this narrative.

My tradition as a poet is deviant you see, a true African sage would weave his or her defence into a bewildering tapestry of tales.
One hundred years ago (is the timing not uncanny?) a young man named Ahmed Chothia lived in Kacholie, a village somewhere in Gujerat, India. He got married when he was barely twenty. It was an arranged marriage, but the young girl was pretty, and not unpleasant, so Ahmed did not complain. Because of economic conditions, had to seek work in the big city (Delhi, Bombay, what does it matter?). He found employment as a clerk in the nascent transport industry goods for England, goods from England, and mostly the latter, given the power relations that existed then). He was glad for the work, as the saying goes, and indeed found comfort and somewhat pious leisure (he always had a devout tendency) in the company of fellow Muslim migrant workers. He worked, and prayed, meditating in the *jamaa* of a few Sufis he had met, remitted money to his family, visited his wife and his first born child regularly. Life would gone on like this, insignificant by the scale of things in "vast and teeming" India, with Ahmed becoming a kind of lay Imam, working during the day and teaching Islamic scripture at night, had history not intervened.
One day he received an urgent message: something "terrible" had happened to his sister Zaybonisha, the family's "baby" a few years younger that he. So urgent did the summons sound that conscientious Ahmed broke a covenant with his employer and left for home in the middle of the day. On the journey home, by train to a siding five miles from his village, on foot from there, or on the back of a rickety cart if he was lucky, Ahmed had a premonition. The terrible thing that had happened to Zaybonisha had something to do with the British military camp close to their village. Everything in and around their village had something to do with the soldiers who lived there, like transient lords, red-faced men who arrived and departed with great regularity. Some were so young they looked like angels, until the sun reddened their faces, and the awareness of their power over the natives turned them into arrogant and overbearing animals.

He found his father in a state of silent fury, Ahmed could only guess at the rage eating Hawai at the placid old man's heart. His mother wept, and his sister averted her face. Soon the other villages gathered and told Ahmed in great detail how young Zaybonisha went to the river with the other young girls form the village, how, as Ahmed knew, the British soldiers always harried and harangued them, but rarely molested them in the physical sense. One young soldier though, seemed to be there each time they went to the river to draw water (this was a time before taps, piped water, or the sinking of boreholes) and wash the family's clothes. His eyes, young but already lascivious, sought out Zaybonisha, only her it seemed, among all the other equally pret girls. He smiled at her with his as yet unfaded freshness, looked crisp and handsome in his uniform. (They looked Hawai when Ahmed's dark looks questioned the closeness with which they seemed to have watched the soldier). One day the village girls were returning home, chatting and laughing, and suddenly Zaybonisha was not with them.
Fearful of going back, the darkness comes so suddenly, they hurried ahead and found some of the village men, who at their urging went in search of the missing girl. They found her, pinned down by the soldier, and thrashing about "like a fish out of water". In this dry part of the country, very few villagers had ever seen a fish thrash about, so Ahmed attributed this to the Islamic learning: surely the Koran teaches one about these things. Anyway, Zaybonisha started to moan and scream. She was in pain, in great pain, the men testifies, it was obvious from the wy she screamed. When the villagers had gone Ahmed observed his sister, saw in her a great shame. Whether or not the soldier had raped her, he had filled her and her family with shame. They could petition the military authorities, molestation of natives was forbidden, but Ahmed knew ther would be no justice. He was a soldier; white, British, Zaybonisha was a woman, young, from a backward village. No matter what happened, whe would be tainted forever.
With the great patience he had learned from the Sufis, he plotted revenge. He watched the camp, observed the patrols, saw the way

they went about in groups when off duty. But he knew that the young soldier would go back to the river, look for Zaybonisha, either to savour the triumph of his conquest, or in sorrow that she had not returned. He would be careful warned by his experienced officer about how savage "these people" were when it came to redressing the real or imagined slights to the honour of their women. Ahmed was patient. He did nothing the first two time he encountered the soldier on his own. The third time Ahmed stunned the man with a blow from a stick hidden in the folds of his flowing Imam-to-be garb, dragged him into the bushes and then throttled him with his sister's silk scarf. A scarf inherited from her mother, the very sacrf that Zaybonisha would one day have worn around her head when she got married. There would be now wedding now, only a woman burdened with shame, a burden that her family would have to bear along with her.

He had planned his escape as meticulously as he had planned his vengeance. He did the body so that it would not be found for at least a week. Enough time for him to collect some precious belongings from his lodgings in the city (his favourite *kitaabs*, a prayer bead reputed to have been brought by an ancestro from conquering Persia), make contact with the Sufis who it seemed had a wide network. He made his way to Goa, where he signed up on a Portuguese ship as cook and scribe for the coolie crew. The ship plied its trade in spice and oils along the African coast. Ahmed jumped ship in Delagoa Bay, now Maputo, made his way torturously up the East coat, avoiding Durban where if the British were looking for him, and if they knew he had made his way to Africa, would look first.

He finally settle in Cape Town, married the daughter of a pious Malay family (she traced her ancestry back to the slaves whom the Dutch brought out from Malaysia and Indonesia), and fathered many children. He bacame a fully-fledged Imam in charge of a Mosque, as pious and as poor as God demanded of the truly faithful. The rest of his history is immaterial, save that his daughter met and married the son of a Dutch woman and another Indian man from Kholvad. A merchant who wold one day put a gun into his mounth simply to fell what death tasted like. That is my African heritage. One of hybridisation, an indelible, irreducible product of history's bastard groin. So, I am African also because I have no choice. I grew up speaking Afrikaans and isi-sotho, and only learned to speak English because my father felt that these local languages had no future. Alas, I cannot speak Gujerati or Urdu, my grandfather's languages. Perhaps there lurks in me my Grandfather's (I am named after him) extreme sense of injustice and recompense, perhaps another, unsung part of my ancestry allows the poet in me to prevail.

A much larger question arises though. Why do we Africans insist on calling ourselves African? Chinese, Indian, Vietnamese of Japanese people would identify themselves by their "nationalities" (political, nation-state identities often as artificial as those imposed on Africa by colonialism) rather than by the secondary, geographical label of "Asian". I have yet to hear a Mexican or a Brazilian say "I am Latin American". Even the term "American", once infused with grandiose ambition by Simon bolivar, has been reduce to describing a (usually white Protestant) citizen of the United States.

Africa is as divided by language, race, tradition and belief as Asia, the Americans and Europe (the European Union is nothing more than a trade cartel masked by cultural pretensions), yet we proclaim being "African" with great pride. From Muammar Gaddafi to Nelson Mandela, to writers like Ngugi waThiongo and Nadine Gordimer, there is no greater honour than being called a "son", and in these egaliatarian times, a "daughter" of Africa. On the negative scale, American scoundrels can only seek refuge in the rather scrawny jingoism of gher nationhood, while their African counterparts have a continental cloak behind which to hide. In Zimbabwe "African-ness" justifies homophobia, in Sudan it condones the brutal excesses of religious fanaticism.

In my native South Africa it unleashes all the skewed –and opportunistic– patriotism that man is capable of. Imagine the spectacle of a white Afrikaner's mortified indignation when his (usually the male species reacts this way) "African-ness" is questioned. Instead of acknowledging the wrongs his people had committed in the name of God and Europe, he would indulge in torturous justifications, ultimately saying: "this was Africa after all". Three hundred years of the systematic destruction of everything indigenous to Africa (language, freedom of cultural association, ancient societal structures and belief systems that supported the weak and the vulnerable) is conveniently forgotten. It reminds one of an angry ostrich, that bird of arid places famous for its self-induced lack of consciousness, feathers fluffed out and fatal hoof ready to strike. It is almost as awesome as the pious sight of a "black" African "offering" his white counterpart recognition in return for political and more importantly, economic atonement. The white ostrich and the black peacock doing their dance of accommodation.

As for pan-African affinity, we are confronted more by more diversity than uniformity. After all, what can slick, smooth talking, bottled-beer drinking Johannesburg sophisticates possibly have in common with Kenya's Massai nomads? Even inside South Africa, the Johannesburg *clevah* is at least a generation apart —in attitude and lifestyle— from his or her own *Kwa-Zulu* rural cousins. In fact the *Kwaito-listening*, Diesel-wearing youth of South Africa share greater state-of-mind and state-of-health similarities with their New York contemporaries than with their peers in Cairo. This is possibly true of Nairobi's young, and even the trendy sons and daughters of the Moroccan middle class may well want to see more cappuccino bars than Mosques in Marrakech.

But yes, Gadaffi and Mandela are right, there is something noble about being an African, despite all the inherent contradictions. It is an intuitive sense of being and belonging, intangible almost. A "feeling" more than a knowledge, and hence, capable of transcending all the painful contradictions, and given the right conditions, of healing the deep ethnic, linguistic and religious schisms that afflict Africans as people.

South Africa is one example of such a 'miracle'. Yes, this term is not mere hyperbole. For the victims of Apartheid to resist their own instincts (sharpened by decades of abuse and humiliation) and forgive their oppressors, and for the oppressors to relent in their own belief (instilled over generations, with fanatic fervour) that Blacks were primitive and incapable of governing this vast and complex country, was indeed miraculous.

But it did not come about by the spontaneous historical combustion or through the sheer utilitarian need to save an economy from ruin: this has not rescued the Congo from the blindness of its protagonists, or diverted Angola from its tragedy of war-to-the-bitter-end. The south African miracle required the courage, the foresight of individuals. It required almost a poet's will to seek out harmony where none seemed posible, a desire and a capacity to speak, in a barren mental desert where people on all sides had learnt only to hear and understand their own, codified language. How close they came, those speaking, thinking individuals, to a failure of words, how often they must have despaired at their inability to capture in true and simple terms the problem confronting them, and hence, the difficulty in constructing solutions that would last!

Ask poets about the anguish they experience when word and music and form refuses to find a natural harmony, about the gruelling hours spent before that horrible piece of paper, struggling to discipline the stubborn infestation of crawling, recalcitrant insects. In the end it is the ability to listen to both the inner and the outer world, to hear with greater clarity the voices of others than even your own, that helps the poet to create a poem of great and simple beaty. Thank God for forbearance, bred in the solitude of prison, of people like Nelson Mandela.

Today, Africa needs the poet's approach more than ever before.

Our challenges are huge, and so often repeated it sounds like a litany of despair: illiteracy, hunger, declining health care, the spread of HIV and AIDS, joblessness and so forth. In reality, there is one problem that either causes all the other conditions of suffering, or at the very least aggravate them, and that is poverty. Being poor is to be disempowered, incapable of withstanding natural disasters or resisting the evil of despots and dictators. It make the gentle callous, the generous selfish, the displaced fearful of other displaced. Poverty reduces humans to the level of savage animals. Witness how xenophobia is sweeping my own country, how those who had been discriminated against because of their colour for decades now discriminate against fellow African because they dress differently and talk differently. Look at how our own government's response to "illegal immigration" begins to resemble the way Americans relate to Mexicans, the British to Pakistanis, how we want to build walls, police jungle boundaries, turn rivers into death traps.

To combat poverty Africans need simple, harmonious solutions well thought out and struggled for as fiercely as we struggled for liberation from racism and colonialism. We will not find those solutions by creating European style "fortress states" (designed primarily to keep Europe white, to keep Africans and Asians out). Perhaps we need to examine our indigenous strengths and build on them, but not remain enslaved to old and outdated notions that cannot survive the rapacious might of European and American economies. Poverty and strife has taught us something: innovation and creativity. It takes vast imagination to survive against all the odds. Why can that ingenuity not be harnessed to create wealth?

For more than fifty years that great African institution the "extended family" has had to endure the strain of Africa's under-development. Governments and private financial institutions shy awai from helping individuals to start enterprises, always preferring "community based" solutions. It is an excuse for doing nothing, invented by development purists from rich Northern countries, and imbibed with unthinking ease by our own planning elites. Africa does have a tradition of individual leadership. Where does Nelson Mandela come from, or Kwame Nkruma, Julius Nyere and countless others? We need to encourage individuals to create wealth, for themselves, for their families and for their communities. This too is an ancient African tradition, usurped by white settlers in order to weaken existing African societies.

Africa will not overcome its poverty unless we develop skilled individuals who can wrench themselves, their families and then their communities out of the cycles of poverty that drag each succeeding generation deeper and deeper into the quagmires of dependency (on international financial institutions, on development aid that robs us of our power to decide what

is appropriate for where we live and the times we live in). We need to stop living our lives, as individuals, as nations, as people waiting for the generosity of international donors to materialise. This sets African up against African in competing for handouts.
Is this a poetic solution, a solution at all? Firstly, it tries at the very least to state our problem in simple terms. Secondly, it demands that we seek new solutions to new problems. Thirdly it will force us to build our "human potential", to inculcate an awareness that we do have the innate potential to excel, and then transform excellence into an additional aspect of our culture. American millionaires pay taxes, emply people, enrich their communities (go and look at London or New York, at rural Sweden or pastoral France, the wealth, nay, the opulence is self-evident), and they have a million millionaires.
Africa need not seek the New Kingdom of the fabulously, rich avaricious individual. We have a greater sense of sharing, of comunal responsibility. We can take the risk and trust those among us who have the imagination, the skills and energy to break out of the prison of poverty.

Agnès Agboton

Emergency

“My story takes flight”, my old grandmother, Navi, would say, beside the embers of the fire where she prepared her rice and her fish.
Three stones prop up the cooking pot, exactly three stones because four would be too many and two would be too few, or so my people say.
A home that is safe and sound is a home with only three stones, and, by the fireside, Navi would begin to tell me her story.

“My story takes flight, up and up, until it comes across a beautiful bee-eater, perched on his branch in a treetop, resting after his long annual journey.
It was days and days ago that he left the far-off lands where the cold is already beginning to set in. Below, far below, he saw the restless expanse of the sea, the fertile lands and the fallow fields that to him looked like a dark stain, but where he would be able to find –as he already knew, this not being his first journey– the insects that he would feed on.
After that came the immense realm of the sands and Ojè, the bee-eater, flew on beneath the burning rays of the sun.”

Navi would then pause to check how her cooking was coming along. Her rice and her fried fish were the best in the market and the hungry would crowd around her stall, where I would sometimes help her to sell her wares. Then she would look at me with eyes full of mischief, because she knew how impatient I was and it pleased her to use the tricks of the veteran storyteller.

“Heeey” she would say “poor bee-eater! His wings had almost given out when the desert began to be peppered with thorn bushes, which meant that at last he could alight carefully on a branch, smooth down his multicoloured plumage with his long bluish beak, so precious to him for hunting insects, and so take rest, knowing that his journey's end lay not too far off, but that he still had a fair way to fly.
But he did not wish to tarry long. There, beyond the lands where the baobab grows, once he had flown over the green cupola of the forest, the clay tracks, the villages where men and women, like multicoloured ants, busied themselves with sowing seed or made their way to the streams

that, from on high, resembled narrow strips of silver; yes, there the warm brightness of the lagoon awaited him and, in its waters, Huè, the carp, the friend he had left behind many months before and with whom he had spent so many good times in conversation."

And Navi would break off once more, taste the spicy sauce that was slowly simmering, thickening, and giving off great bubbles that burst on the surface, and interject with one of those moralistic comments that so infuriated me:

"It is good to have a friend when you arrive somewhere. You can have a roof over your head to sleep under, and you can cast aside your solitude. Yes, it is good to have friends".

Her voice would then merge with the crackling of the firewood.

"After his long journey, Ojè landed in the mangrove swamp that sank into the lagoon, in the exact same spot where he had so often chatted to his friend Huè, the carp. And he did not have long to wait before seeing the fish's round and supple mouth appear on the water's surface.
When the two friends meet up, their hearts are filled with a breath of fresh air, and they search then for the words of days gone by, the things that they had said to each other and which have remained unsaid for so long.
'Are you still not able to fly?' asked the bee-eater when they were through with their lengthy greetings. 'You must leave these murky waters once and for all. That's what I told you last year. Emerge! That way you will be able to accompany me, you will learn the secrets of the land and the air, you will see from on high how small things appear and you will discover how they are made. Emerge and come along with me. You can do it.'
And Huè, the carp, felt that once again something was stirring within her. She saw her friend perched high up in the tree, admired his multicoloured plumage, listened to the wonders of which he spoke, imagined the places that Ojè had visited and that, if she stayed in the lagoon where she had been born, Huè, the carp, would never come to know any of this."

Then Navi would pause to look at me, forgetting about her cooking pots for a few moments and, although hard to believe, let me assure you, she would make a face like a bee-eater. "Emerge!" she'd cry in a rasping voice, "Emerge!" And I could so easily picture the bird with his haughty manner, so stuffed full of knowledge, so puffed up with learning, and the sad humbleness of the carp who, as Navi would go on to tell, made an enormous effort to leave the murky waters of the mangrove swamp.

"For many, many days" (Navi's voice would return to normal and, as she spoke, she would cast a little more firewood in between the three stones of the hearth), "for days and yet more days, Ojè, the bee-eater, repeated his exhortation. 'Emerge! Emerge!' And his friend the carp first stuck her head out of the water, then tried to make a great leap, hanging there for a few seconds above the warm waters, with all her scales shimmering in the sun.

At last, one fine day, while the bee-eater kept on egging her on 'Emerge, emerge!', Huè took such a huge leap that she fell, flailing, onto the bank. Ay yay yay! That was really terrible, because the carp had not yet learned how to breathe the air through which her friend could fly, and so she stayed there, on the bank, gasping as if she were about to die until, with a great swish of her tail, she finally managed to get back to the lagoon. Then Ojè said to her 'You'll learn, it's not so difficult. Little by little you will learn how to breathe just like me, you will leave that absurd place down there and you will learn, with my help, that the world is immense. You will see the most beautiful landscapes. You will learn the nature of all things. You will learn, mark my words. Emerge!'

And the carp tried time and time again. Little by little she began to discover that she could breathe, little by little she became accustomed to the air and each time she managed to stay longer on the stony riverbank, no longer needing the waters of the lagoon for survival.

'Emerge, emerge!' the bee-eater kept on saying, celebrating the progress his friend the fish was making, with shouts of joy and laughter.

It was hard, indeed it was, harder than my burden of having to prepare the food each morning to take to market for others to devour (and Navi, my poor grandmother, would then hold her hands to her aching kidneys and stand up with the boiling cooking pot in her hands), it was hard, but Huè learned how to breathe while in the air and soon, little by little, by using the fins on both sides of her body, and by flapping them very strenuously and very fast, she managed some short flights. Brief at first and not too high, then ever longer and ever higher.

'You see? You have emerged. Now fly, fly alongside me!' cried the bee-eater, full of joy.

And so she did, and so it came to be.

One afternoon, while the short-lived sunset tinged the lagoon red, the carp made it to the top branch of the tree, where her friend Ojè was waiting for her.

She was very, very tired and the bee-eater made up a bed of leaves and branches for her so that she could sleep. That was her first night out of the water.

The days that followed, after a new day had dawned that surprised her at the very top of a tree, were full of discoveries and strange emotions for the carp. Although it was not too difficult for her after all her efforts, she first had to learn to balance on a branch, because, unlike Ojè the bee-eater, she did not have feet that she could hang on with. She finally managed it and, like her friend, she could look down upon the earth from on high, and she learned about the works of man, about the power of fire, about the strange machines that criss-crossed dusty roads or flew through the air or sailed the endless moving waters, so different from those of her native lagoon.

Her native lagoon! On one particular night, the memory of the calm and cloudy warmth of those waters that used to softly caress her scales came back to her, and she longed to roam once more through the tangled forests of sunken mangrove swamps, the tender seaweed groves that slowly swayed as gently as a breeze, the dark and tiny caverns where the river mud offered her protection and food; she longed to experience once again the pleasant sensation of gliding along effortlessly and of feeling the mysterious brush against her skin of that wet and opaque universe in which she had always lived.

And then she knew that she was homesick.

So she turned to Ojè, her friend the bee-eater, who had taught her to breathe while in the air, who had taught her to fly, who had shown her the

way to emerge and had given her the power to leave the water, and she asked Ojè to accompany her on her return to the lagoon. And they both flew off and, on reaching the river bank, the carp fell laughing into the waters, which welcomed her as if they had been waiting for her all along.
Ojè remained there on a branch for a long time while his friend relived the pleasures of yesteryear, and only some days later was he able to see, on the water's surface, the round mouth of Huè, the carp that had learned to fly.
Then he heard her call out 'What are you doing up there, still on that branch? Come on, submerge!'
And then she went on to describe for him the fragrant paradise that was waiting in the waters. The gentle swaying of the seaweed, the pleasures of the warm water brushing against one's back.
'Submerge!' she finally cried. 'You'll see, it's not so difficult.'
But Ojè has yet to submerge; the waters of the lagoon terrify him, he fears that his feathers will be stained by the mud and he assures his friend the carp that, were he to submerge, he would not know how to breathe.
'Don't worry!' says Huè again. 'It doesn't matter, you'll learn! Submerge! You'll see the soft light of...'
Time and again the bee-eater turns away, proudly preens his feathers and pretends to despise the treasures that his friend offers him. Or perhaps he really does despise them".

I suspect that my grandmother, Navi, used to keep the story in step with the cooking of her rice and her sauce, prolonging it or curtailing it depending on the task in hand, because, every time she recounted it, upon reaching this point, she would point me in the direction of one of the steaming earthenware bowls, place the other on her head and we would both set off down the road to market.
Only after having walked a good distance would Navi then stop.

"Perhaps one day" she'd say, panting, "Ojè, the bee-eater, will learn to submerge."

And she would hurry along on her way.

Aly Diallo

At the point of intersection of centuries and millennia: the free discourse of a Malian

A question has been put to me, and I must answer. I'll be happy to answer, with my well-sated boa's mouth. But first, let me rinse out my mouth, for before speaking, it is necessary to take some precautions. If a man must speak of the past, he should try to avoid awakening old demons. And if he wants to speak of the future, he must watch out for new evil spirits. It is always difficult to speak of the past or the future; everyone knows this, except our rulers. To enable them to fully understand, let us examine the question put to me.

"Between two centuries", I was told.

"Between two chairs", responded the sceptical *cora*, accompanied by *balafós* and other instruments.

Traditional musicians have this great quality: they have no fear of anyone, not even of the Chief.

"Between two centuries", I shouted.

A voice emerged from amongst those present.

"The subject is intelligent and the question is full of interest. But still it deserves to be framed more precisely".

"Between two centuries, the free discourse of an African from Mali", I suggested.

"Between two centuries, the failed discourse of a Malian from Africa", growled the *cora* player.

"To your places musicians. For a sated boa, all this is mere chatter, the tales of *cowboys*. Time is colourless, odourless and insipid. It slips away eternally, everlastingly until the end of chaos. It is the only thing that truly has time to waste. Some wish it would go more quickly, others wish that it would slow down a little. Every day marks the end of a century. Every tomorrow marks the dawning of a new millennium. But fools there will always be who believe in the symbolism of the intersection of centuries and millennia".

Those present gazed at me astounded, as if I had gone off at a tangent.

Well. At this turn of the century, it is a good idea to look at things from the point of view of Zimbabwe, Uganda or all of the Congos. But it is even better to stick to our own history and above all to examine our own consciences.

Ah, well! Is that what you were asking me to do?

What happens here has come from elsewhere. That's how Africa is. Since the dawning of time, man has not invented anything. There is a lack of imagination. Africa's speciality is dealing with the everyday, with what is. Here, innovation is not considered as a technique for development. We borrow, we happily import everything, especially since the invention of the photocopier.

Immediately the musicians struck up the Song of the Ass, which brays wildly and bucks when free, but never when it is loaded with its burden.

"Stop that music", I shouted again.

Then there was silence, a long silence in which I breathed heavily.

"Is it a new ruse that the West has prepared for us? Isn't it a trap that once more entices us?"

"In any case, we have always fallen into their snares. All our Chiefs do is puff themselves up to give us a complex, but never to solve a problem," retorted the *sanza* man.

In reality, Africans never believe anyone's fine words, no matter how humane they might be. We always find what has not been said, something that betrays the speaker. For the whole world has lied to us throughout the 20th century, and before that as well.

My chest, full of air, deflated like a rubber balloon. Then I asked the musicians to play *tignè*, the truth. And the *tignè* floated up into the air, like the flight of migrating birds in search of a more welcoming place when the weather threatens.

To fully understand all this let us look to time, a little like the Roman *Pontifex Maximus*, who long ago also appealed to time.

And now I have rinsed out my mouth with the foetid water of the village pond, listen to me! Whether I speak truly or mistakenly, it all forms part of the search for truth. But two things deceive us: forgetfulness and lying, and sometimes silence. Let's begin then at the beginning.

The past is the past, as we know. That is why we recount it. The present is present; we can remove its shell and examine it. But the future...

"So, the African 20th century?".

That came after enslavement. Having barely stepped out of the boat of natural history, the black man was thrust onto the train of civilisation. On his "involuntary departure" to discover the limits of the ocean, he found himself experiencing the virtues of the new civilisation: that of paying for his annual ration of oxygen, and of working for free, under the ever-watchful eye of the *rabble* guard. This, then, was the civilisation of colonialisation, though perhaps I have overlooked some of its other tricks.

"It wasn't at all Catholic", my ex-combatant grandfather confided to me one day, "But it is the sad truth".

And immediately the memories began to spill out.

"Ah, yes... There was also the First World War –the price of the blood, they said. It was necessary to pay for the red blood spilt by the white colonists who died while civilising Africa. This was the 'Call to Africa'. To lay glittering rails through the scorching hot mountains of the arid lands of tropical Africa was good, but it was not enough. It was also necessary to step out onto the battlefield".

"How many friends did you lose?" I asked him.

He didn't remember exactly.

"Many, many, too many," he replied thoughtfully, "And when we came back, we had scarcely disembarked on the coasts of West Africa, when we had to embark once more for the Second World War. This time I went with my son, to defend the 'motherland'".

But after the war, with the motherland saved, when the whole world shrank back into itself to lick its wounds, something terrible happened. It was when the UN was established, to be exact when the UNESCO was created. Though possibly making a mistake in his choice of scenario, Torres Bodet proposed, on behalf of the Mexican delegation, the programming of the education of the people who lived in protectorates or under colonial rule and of those who lived in the mandated territories. Supported by the French delegate, Léon Blum, the response of the British Prime Minister Attlee was clear, too clear: the question of the education of the inferior races was not a matter for the UNESCO, but rather for a Tutelary Commission of the United Nations. An example of the supreme contempt in which civilisation held the barbarians, whilst still strictly observing the universal rights of western man.

The injuries have undoubtedly caused deep wounds. And although these may heal, they leave scars, which do not easily disappear. That is why the African is not a man like others. He has suffered in his own flesh for many, many years as a result of the colour of his skin. Never was a truer word spoken! A man with a permanently cricked neck, who cannot even see what is behind him by looking in the rear-view mirror, who must instead be given a sounding board to enable him to contemplate the stalagmites in the caverns of the past. A sleepwalker who stumbles forward without perceiving the future. Never was a truer word was spoken!

The musicians remained in absolute silence. They could not bear to hear more. I went on alone with what remained of my story.

"Liberty, Equality, Fraternity", is a slogan for the colonisers, not for the colonised. That was when the blacks understood that they would never be men as in the Rights of Man, and so they went on pretending to be fools. This was the beginning of the movements for decolonisation.

But the white man has never wanted to admit that decolonisation meant the decolonisation of both the colonised and the coloniser. It was then that the Africans understood that no matter how hard they tried to be English, Spanish, French or Portuguese, they would never be more than second-class citizens. They began to read in the stars and to play with cowries to try to discern where their "true home" lay. And the decolonisation movements were swiftly transformed into struggles for independence.

The African cadres who made up the colonial *petite bourgeoisie* went to stir up their respective tribes. Believing in the return of feudalism, the tribal chiefs set about restoring and reactivating the broken mechanisms of the old traditions. The awakening of the tribes did nothing to reassure the small or the great intellectuals of Africa. The tribal space, feudal *par excellence*, is not a comfortable place for a *petite bourgeoisie*. It is too narrow. The arms of the lower middle classes are the workers' organisations, and where these are lacking, armed struggle. Setting themselves, then, above the tribal chiefs, the teachers, the nurses, the clerks, the postal workers, the forestry workers and shop-keepers set about organising and mobilising society and propelling it towards a new space: the nation.

The existence of these two blocks precipitated events. And then came independence. The new nation was born and the *petite bourgeoisie* of colonial times became the *bourgeoisie* of the nation. The African cadres were so much at ease that, overnight, they forgot everything. Democracy and the multi-party system, long ago learnt in the parliaments of the metropolitan powers, were quickly pushed away into the cupboard. The Single Party marked the direction and became the only form of expression. They even forgot to create a place that was acceptable to the officers, to those of lower rank, to the corporals and soldiers who returned from the far-flung corners of metropolitan power in Algeria, Indochina and elsewhere. However, in a society, even if it is well organised, the armed forces are the supreme force, the most disciplined sector and the best-equipped force on the ground. Since they felt marginalised, the men of the armed forces decided to make their presence felt. In the great dividing up of power, they demanded their share of the cake. Only natural! And then we are surprised that there have been so many *coups d'état* in Africa! The shrewdest Heads of State opted for semi-independence:

"Set about the tasks of your administration, but don't ask the armed forces to move," they demanded in the name of the "motherland".

But look what happened. After independence, you had to pay not only for your annual ration of oxygen, but also the tax on animals, including cows and goats. The collectivised countryside replaced forced labour. Low salaries doled out grudgingly did not satisfy the demands of the unions. The successive droughts did nothing to help. The rural exodus led to the proliferation of shantytowns. The growing impoverishment spread misery ever more widely. Everybody was struggling to get by till the end of the month. Arrogant and covetous, the Single Party simply ignored the existence of the new national *petite bourgeoisie*, even though it had favoured its emergence. Despite the strikes and the many claims made, the Single Party little cared about the dreams of emancipation that this new opposition harboured.

Reduced to their final entrenchment, the most impatient amongst the national *petite bourgeoisie* personally took up Kalachnikovs, and stirred up the tribe of the disinherited. The war of the Tuareg in Mali was the only means open to the turbaned leaders of the administration and the multitude of unemployed desert dwellers of imposing their claims on the Single Party. But in their blind greed, the national *bourgeoisie* would not even deign to concede a stipend to this alternative *gendarmerie*.

The collapse of the Eastern Bloc surprised many an African and disrupted many projects. The French discourse at La Baule complicated matters. By tying French aid, from then on, to the process of democratising the African states, Mitterrand caught the monarchs of the Single Parties off-guard and disarmed the rebellions –a godsend for the *petite bourgeoisie* of the capitals and urban centres. Against the Single Party in power, the teachers, doctors, judges and union bosses meticulously put together and mobilised an army of workers, of the unemployed, of beggars and students with no future. And all the workless in the Republic set out to bring down the monolith of the Single Party. The National Conference and the Transitional Government paved the way for the birth of democratic Mali.

Dozens of political parties were formed. The atmosphere surrounding the elections was so relaxed that nobody challenged the results of the first legislative and presidential processes. Democratisation began to transform the society, when suddenly everything ground to a halt. Instead of advancing, the new Chiefs began to reverse things. The present which had been so full of hope, suddenly became as complicated as the past. The traditional reflex action of those in power to do what is necessary to maintain power ruined the game. The euphoria of refound freedom swiftly evaporated. Democracy began to turn sour.

"*Tignè*", exclaimed the man who was playing the *tam-tam,* "Why are you hiding your face with your fingers apart?"

The musicians immediately struck up.

"The present is the only place about which man can tell the truth", observed the *sanza* man.

Now that I was beginning to broach the subject of the present –holding fast to *el tignè*, the truth– I was really a free man. And the musicians started to play better and better. They are like introverted transvestites, these people. They can't bear to hear even a tiny lie. And so I took up the microphone once more.

“My country is in itself the encapsulation of all the hopes and failures of Africa”.

Those present listened attentively.

“A long time ago now, Mali was proclaimed the best democratic model in Africa. Some people still parade around the world on the strength of this, even though the promise has worn thin now. The truth is that it only took five years to return to the ‘Single Political Line’. The electoral tricks and manipulations in 1997 saw to that, despite the presence of international observers. On the other hand, I am not too keen on the presence of these foreigners at our great electoral celebrations, even if the presence of an adult is always necessary in a kindergarten. It’s time for our political leaders (both in the government and in the opposition) to grow up”.

The audience applauded and the music galvanised the crowd even more.

“The present is gloomy”, I concluded.

“You haven’t proved anything”, the *cora* player muttered.

“Do you want proof?”

Mali is a great and very beautiful country, with a history that is as great as Kilimanjaro, a culture as vast as the Pacific Ocean. It is impossible to pass from the Middle Ages to modern times without passing through my country. Have you heard of Kankan Moussa? The man, whose fabulous wealth forced the devaluation of the Cairene currency when he passed through Mecca in the 14th century. He came from Mali. And Timbuktu? That important intellectual, commercial and religious centre of the 15th and 16th centuries? It is in Mali. In this country, full of history and culture, there is no longer a single festival, not a single exhibition, that can be called a popular event. Only a few foreigners take part, motivated as they are by the needs of the cause. From being a land of cultural creation, Mali is becoming a land of mere cultural gesticulation.

In terms of education, far from consolidating and developing the experience already built up, time is wasted in debates that are as useless as they are sterile. Instead of evolving, discussion simply goes round and round in circles. After long and stormy debates, a university was set up in 1997, and its Main Hall is the auditorium of the Palace of Culture.

“Do you want more examples?”

“Yes”, answered the public, “This time economic ones”.

In the years 1940-50, French Sudan was the granary of West Africa. Today, Mali imports rice from Asia. Since 1960, the year in which my country obtained its independence, not a single kilometre of new rails has been laid on the old *Dakar-Niger* railway, at least not on the section that lies within Mali. The rolling stock was renewed at some stage, but it is still ancient, as if they were cattle wagons. Even worse, not a single quarter goes by without a derailment. They even talk about using accident-damaged rolling stock from Europe; a gift from Heaven! Navigation on the great Niger river...

“Now we want social examples!” shouted the public.

“You want social examples?”

Fine! Low salaries are always in fashion. For lack of imagination, our great leaders have simply subscribed to the policy of structural adjustment, with its panoply of dismissals and price rises. To take on new workers is impossible. Access to finance for micro-projects is still just a dream. To be unemployed is no longer a source of shame. Misery is everywhere. On all the streets, on every corner, you see a festival of beggars. Mere survival has become the common denominator in our society.

One day, while waiting at some traffic lights at a crossroads, surrounded on all sides by men and women selling carrots and brooms, I asked myself if all this was not somehow the hallmark of poverty. Of course it is necessary to work in order to make a living, but this kind of commerce smacks of begging. A misery that seeks to hide its name.

"That's enough for now," said the *cora* player. "Tomorrow will also be another day", observed the *balafó* man.

"Then, we will leave it here for this evening and we will see each other again tomorrow".

That night, a vague feeling crept over me. What came into my mind was a mediocre, bitter idea. I caught myself wondering whether my country was not withering away, like a delicate flower. It is necessary for us Malians to calm down. It is necessary for us to control ourselves. We will be wasting our time if we seek, at all costs, to reaffirm ourselves by comparing ourselves to others. It is necessary to stir consciences. The form of development that our political and administrative leaders have conceived, and are applying, will inevitably lead to stagnation. The macro-economic results may give Mali's leaders international credibility, but they do not feed the hungry of Mali. They do not look after the ill. True development involves the permanent solution of the real problems of society. We need to learn to develop on our own terms.

Endogenous development? Absolutely not. There are, according to Aimé Césaire, two ways to lose yourself: to live curled up into yourself, or to dissolve yourself in the universal. Mali would lose greatly if it closed in on itself. It would gain little if it were to become just a digital appendage to the world. The priority for the great majority of my compatriots, and indeed for every human being, is to be healthy, to be able to eat one's fill, to work and to sleep peacefully at home.

On the threshold of the third millennium, the urgent needs of Mali in the 21st century are easily identifiable. The rooting of democracy, and social peace, are primordial. Only a sack that is empty, like an empty stomach, cannot stand up on its own. The fight against poverty and in favour of health, education, training and employment must be the priorities in the framework of any rethinking of development policy. The fight against corruption is a major imperative. The annual loss to the State of Mali caused by corruption alone has been estimated at between five and ten thousand million CFA Francs. A State Comptroller General that regulates, and a Justice system that respects its oaths could, without much effort, eradicate this plague, so long as political leaders made a firm non-partisan commitment, understanding that there is no such thing as a good corrupt individual.

But development also means developing a culture of development. The "artificial" underemployment of the cadres who twiddle their thumbs all day long, and the slowness of the administration, are just as serious blights as corruption. It would be to the benefit of good government everywhere if the ethic of work well done were cultivated. The spirit of initiative and the mastery of the techniques of innovation also form part of the culture of development. The innumerable seminars offering information, training or retraining should leave considerable room for evaluation and innovative creativity. Lyrical speeches will change nothing.

A new century is beginning, without fanfares, but full of hopes and fireworks. The boa's mouth of the new millennium gapes, allowing a glimpse of a dark tunnel. The future century and millennium are great because they are symbolic. But symbolism is a complex discourse, whose reading always involves the combination of relationships between the subject, the signifier and the signified. The route map for the third millennium is still vague. The shape of the 21st century remains ill-defined, despite or perhaps because of the contradictory discourses of the experts. Everything indicates that we are entering an open space. And an open space is not only open to all our hopes, but also to all sorts of dangers. There will be many important steps forward, but it is possible that there will also be steps back. The official optimism does not reassure me. We must be watchful. The press and all the intellectuals of Mali must man the parapets and participate in the promoting of a true culture of development.

Dakar, 20 April 2000

Ama Ata Aidoo

A fairly grey dawn

In the grand tradition of writers, I hope to do two things in this paper: raise some questions that I cannot pretend to have answers for, and then support my line with a couple of quotations from my writings.

On July 11th 1998, I was struck by a bold headline on page 7 of *The Spectator*, an Accra weekly. "The story of Breman Asikuma", it screamed. When I tried to read the piece, my heart sank immediately. It began with "A legend has it...". Something about that opening did not sound right. This was two years to the end of the whole of the 20th century, and an entire millenium. Meanwhile, Breman Asikuma is not a lost continent like Atlantis, or some dead, disappeared, and completely untraceable city in ancient Ghana. It is a small but quite busy rural town in contemporary southern Ghana. There are houses there, and schools, and markets. There are also women, men and children living their everyday lives. Every now and then, someone dies in the town, and gets buried. In fact, according to Maxwell Adjei-Mensah, the autor of the piecee, "it is one of the popular towns in the Central Region because of its outstanding activities". Among other sterling attributes, this town is the hub of a leading cocoa farming district. I persisted and finished reading the article, only to conclude that the entire piece was a rather sketchy and vague attempt to tell the history of the town, especially how it came by its name. I was appalled. I wondered why any story about such a town should still be a legend? I was thinking that certainly by now, every Ghanaian should know, as a matter of course, the precise and detailed history of this and any other Ghanaian town. That we should not have to rely on some vague and sketchy legends that are so ridiculously simple, that any child can put them together to explain the names of places. Besides, if as in this case, the history of any human settlement is linked to any wars and their aftermaths, we should know which ones: who fought whom, when they were fought, and other essential details about them. In an account of this nature, just mentioning some heavy data in passing, like the autor of this piece did with the "Ashanti Wars" (sic!), is not good enough.

It occurred to me them, that the apparent ignorance of our own historical data is not only common, but in fact, might even be typical of us, Ghanaians, (West Africans, Africans, all other people of African descent). Ask for the origins of any village, town or city, and invariably, someone begins with "legend has it...". Legend is definitely not history. It is some grey principle that can oly provide the shadow of information, which we are not under any obligation to trust. It is 'a traditional story sometimes popularly regarded as historical but not authenticated.' Therefore, depending solely on legends to explain our past is a way of not owning that past; or owning up to it. We are abrogating any responsibility for that past.
So then, what is it about our past that frightens, or embarrasses us so? What are we so shy about? What are we afraid of? What happened to us? Who did what to us, how and when? Even more crucially, what did we do to ourselves, and one another? We have got to confront these questions. We need to know about, and deal with, our past in all its mad, glorious or painful details. After all, it is the only one we've got. As the Akans (of Ghana) insist, "the set of teeth in an individual's mouth is the only set each of us has got. So if yours, is yellow that's all you've got to lick". It must surely be obvious that no people can run awai from their history and amount to much. This must be because, to begin with, history is memory, and memory is the mind. Therefore, if we cannot function without either our minds of memories, then we cannot function without our history. Visit any patients who suffer from the illness that is memory loss, now generally known as Alzheimer's, and medically identified as dementia. They do not function. Most of them just sit. According to scientists, the reason why we are able to operate –as humans– at any given time, on any given day, is because we had functioned earlier in similar ways. It is the same whether we went fishing, harvested cocoa, sat in a meeting or edited a film. Our minds automatically remember these activities from the last hour, or the previous day, and remind our different body parts to function similarly today and hopefully, tomorrow too. If, as individuals,

memory is what it takes to even get out us of bed in the morning, then clearly, we weaken ourselves collectively as a people, by not looking for, and dealing with our history. Collective memory or history must be one of the most potent instruments for every society's health and development. It is a most precious possession, since without it, a community can hardly move. Like all precious possessions, we too have to look for ours, and take care of it. If we do not, some other people will snatch it, and worse, use it against us. In the event, we would not even have the energy, or the moral right to call them thieves.

Meanwhile, Africans should take heart. Other peoples' histories are no less nasty or more painful than our own. Other people have not suffered less from their kinsmen's hands. We are no worse than anybody else. We have not been more cruel, less sensisitive or greedier than other people. Ask the Chinese or the Indians or the Europeans. Or better still, we should read about them. We might not believe what they have suffered from their neighbours, or their extended family members.

Of course, we cannot rejoice in the fact that other human beings have been bad, or that all human societies have been terrible at some point or other. But we can take courage from that knowledge and confront our past with it. Besides, we were not responsible for every ugly thing that happened to us in the past. Indeed, the truth is that over the last five hundred or so years, whether enslaved in the Caribbean and the Americans, or colonized in Africa, we as a people have been wronged than we have wronged ourselves.

So we should relax. Or chill, as some cool young cats would tell us. However damning our past is, it is also when we study it properly that we can deal competently with it. Furthermore, it is only when we can deal competently with the past, that we stand any chance of avoiding some of the mistakes taht were made, if not all. When we look at the Europeans, and their First and Second World Wars (which some are describing more appropriately, as the First and Second Great European Tribal Wars of the 20th Century!), we would wonder how, after all that they

did to one another, they could come together economically and politically, and in a space of only fifty years? Part of the answer is that nobody has been allowed to forget the details of earlier devastating conflicts. One extremely potent medium that has been effectively employed to keep the memory of the horrors of war alive is film. For example, it is almost as if the entire British film industry was established to make movies about tose two large-scale European wars of the last century. The Europeans definitely seem to have understood once and for all time, that you can never say "never again" about anything, unless you are in no doubt as to how absolutely dreadful whatever it was, was!
By contrast, we Africans seem to have perfected the development and maintenance of collective amnesia about the past: good or bad. Below is a dramatised version of one form of our people's standard, in-denial attitude to those aspects of our past that are painful. To the eponymous Anowa's persistent attempts to know who had built the massive forts that now stand on the shores of Ghana, and what they had been planned for, the following is all she can get from her grandmother:

"You ask too many questions..."

"Shut up, child or your mouth will twist up one day with questions!..."

"What devil has entered into you, child?"

"It is not good that a child should ask big questions..."

"You frighten me, child..."

"No one talks of these things anymore! All good men and women try to forget; they have forgotten!"

We do not seem to do any better when confronted with a complex past either, not even when that past was glorious, and the memory of it can only ennoble us. The following is a small piece from the page that introduce the concluding section of the four episodes that make up the novel Our Sister Kill Joy or Reflections from a Black-Eyed Squint:

“Said an anxious African-American student to a visiting African professor:

– Sir, please, tell me: is Egypt in Africa?

– Certainly –replied the professor.

– I mean Sir, I don’t mean to kind of harrass you or anything –pressed the student– but did the Egyptians who built the pyramids, you know, the Pharoahs and all, were they African?

– My dear young man –said the visiting professor– to give you the answer your anxiety demands, I would have to tell you a detailed history of the African continent. And to do that, I shal have to speak everyday, twenty-four hours a day, for three thousand years. And I don’t mean to be rude to you or anything, but who has that kind of time?”

Some of us are convinced that such attitudes are not only unhelpful, but positively dangerous. It is also true, however partially, that our lack of confidence in the area of historical claims is based on some hard and concrete realities. One of these “realities” confronting Africans and people of African descent everywhere is that what little attempt is being made to reclaim their history is met with fierce resistance from the mainstream. “Mainstream” here is definitely an euphemism to describe the centres of power in he Euro-American world, and the heirs of our erstwhile slave/colonial masters. The charge is that black historians are in the process of creating a “feelgood history”. This line of judgement is laughable, not because it is untrue, but because it overlooks the fact that all history is feelgood history. If history was indeed the monolithic, uinbiased representation of past events to all people, everywhere, at all time, that we would wish it was, someone’s victory strike would not be another’s massacre. The difference –always– is in the mode of construction.
Mainstream history is constructed as part of the normal business of living: on school curricula, in the academy, at learned conferences, from well-funded research projects; by decently-endowed historical

societies and as subjects of scholarly papers published in respectable journals. On the other hand, since no one is particularly listening, the history of conquered peoples and all manner of marginalised gropus has to be literally screamed from the rooftops. Or at least, form some 'shrill' platform or another. As a result, historians representing such groups invariably ran the risk of getting charghed with "demagoguery", expounding "half-baked theories", and 'making claims' that at best are "not authenticated", and at worst, "spurious". Quite often, the disapproval of the masters took even more concrete forms (like rejection of scholarly Works, as in Ph. D teces) or/and denial of promotions, and invitations to important meetings. It is precisely such challenges that had produced the evasiveness, lack of confidence, and sometimes dowright fear, in the very (African) scholars who should have led the search for our lost pasts. The foregoing is not only relevant to the field of history. The controversy is equally aplicable to the literary and artistic arenas too.

What is really worrying though, is that in spite of the fact that the contentious 20th Century is gone (allelujah!) here in Africa, the new centruy feels normal (as in old, and miserable) especially when we begin counting the well-known woes, and one or two very new ones.

There is peace in Sierra Leone which only needs nine thousand troops to police. We are getting more blood-curling rumbles in Burundi and Rwanda. The fighting among the fascinating array and computation of factions in the Democratic Republic of Congo has not ended inspite of all the peace accords. The only new news worth sharing about that poor rich country is that the press in Africa is bored with the length of the name. So eveywhere these days, it is DRC.

What is horribly new about Africa is what is happening to Southern Africa, especially Mozambique. It is water torture form Mother Nature. Neverending downpours that produce floods that submerge whole villages and towns? Followed immediately by ciclones that bring more water to submerge more villages and towns? Floodwaters that refuse to flow into the sea, but instead, "ebb and flow" and in the process drown

thousands of people? In Africa? Now, do honestly give me a break!... Yet it must be true. "Otherwise the BBC will not report it".
So the time has come for us to stop crowing: those of us who always insisted that Africa was more stable than other continents; as well as those who used that supposed stability as one more explanation of why we have recently been so developmentally lethargic. If we thought that Africa was permanently spared the horrors of the more cataclysmic manifestations of nature's energies, we have got a think coming. We never seemed to know the positive potentials of our land. And if we did, we did not care to harness them for our own use. Clearly, here is another area where we were ignorant. We new nothing about the mysteries and the negative potentials of our environment.
Not that we can blame much on natural disasters. Not yet, anyway. The prize for that goes clearly to our post/neo-colonial rulers. How can anybody be the President of a country, and for twenty years, just oversee the gradual but certain disintegration of the country's economy, and then turn around to ask the same people for a further gift of four or eight or twelve more years! And the tricks are the same whether the plea for more time is by way of general elections or a referendum. They are more clear in the village: especially the women. So when my aunt heard it, her response was: "What? More years? I would like to ask him this. What does he think he can do in four or eight or twelve more years which he could not do in twenty?... Ebei, o! Even Kweku Ananse would not tell such a story and expect to be believed. They must think we are goats".
Is it any wonder that contemporary African generations appear to be afflicted by a heavy dose of the cynicism of a depressing kind? The buzz is that from the thoroughfares of Accra, Harare and Kampala, the majority of young people have almost given up on themselves and on life. Obviously, the refusal of African leadrship to trust our people and trust in their energies is beginning to show. Nobody invested in the youth of Africa. The World Bank seriously recommended a programme of systematic disinvestment in education, health and other vital areas.

Our governments listened well, got the message, and promptly acted on them: Commas, colons and full-stops. The only punctatuion marks missing in the approach were question marks! Meanwhile, those of us who claimed to understand what was going on felt either paralysed to do anything, or actively refused to intervene. And none of our contortions were lost on the young people around us. As one very politely articulate student recently put it: “Madam, you were the Minister of Education in a government. You left after one and a half years. Have you told us what happened? All we know is that since then, you have refused to live in Ghana porperly!”

After this, what forgiveness?

And then, there are the refugees. Or what the UN and her agencies describe as “internally displaced persons”. Africa’s populations had suffered the most unbelievable indignities and humiliations. After a while, we stopped talking about political repression. Most Africans thought that was a normal state of being. Like they thought they thought the state of being in violence was normal under the ancient tyrants and later under the colonial regimes. Belgium and its King Leopold were just the grosser versions. The French, the Portuguese and the Brits had been no better: just a little more subtle. They wielded a civilized brutality. But at least in all those earlier circumstances, they stayed where they were. These days, they are forced to move. So they move, as in *A Modern African Story*. Yes, strange as it may sound, it is true.

I got deported this morning from my home, my village, my country and the land which my forefathers and foremothers bled for, and tilled from the beginning of time.

My crime?

I look like My Cousin from across the border, and His President and My Prime Minister do not see eye to eye.

My Brother the Profesor protests that theoret cally and linguistically, "it simply doesn't make sense! No one can be deported from their native country".

I was packing as he was talking.

I had no time to stop and tell him to look around.

In a land where former freedom fighters are vagrants, or buy respectability only by guarding the property for tose they mortgaged their youths to fight against, the factories and the homes they crawled at night –in the good old days– to burn...

One can be deported from one's birthplace.

And I was.

This morning.

Aminata Sow Fall

Africa: the long march towards the third millennium

The phantoms awoken by the arrival of the year 2000 seem to have fallen asleep once again, worn out by the inexorable pass of time. The 2000 Effect, which for months kept the whole world in suspense, was never felt. The apocalypse proclaimed by some visionaries did not come to pass, thankfully! Nothing then can impede the dawning of the third millennium being inscribed within the logic of all the great periods of human history. The transition will take place against a backdrop of questions, of fears and doubts, but also –why not?– of hopes and great ambitions. In fact, it is the destiny of Mankind to be confronted, at every crossroads, with the inevitable question: which way should we go?

At the gateway to the third millennium we will still be formulating the same question, for despite the fabulous conquests achieved by human intelligence, we have still not resolved all the challenges that confront us. The important advances in the fields of science, technology and the cultivation of the human spirit have not served to eliminate the plagues that spring up like poisonous toadstools across the fields of bitter, hard-won battles.

Despite the undoubted improvements in living conditions and the undeniable results obtained in all those fields that it is necessary to master in order to ensure harmonious integration and social development, there still remain areas of darkness. Human misery rubs shoulders with opulence, barbarity reigns, despotism and oppression wreak havoc, obscurantism, bound up with beliefs, with religion or with the concept of clan, at times goes hand in hand with ever more sophisticated means of sowing terror and unheard-of forms of violence. And all this is happening at the end of a century in which the stupendous advances made since the beginning of time should have allowed us once and for all to lay to rest those demons that are capable of precipitating the world into psychological and moral chaos.

The state of the planet, then, reveals a blatant contradiction. On the one hand, there are the very considerable means, heroically accumulated to ensure the well-being of humanity and, on the other, the open gangrenous wounds that affect millions and millions of people throughout

the world, in the underdeveloped countries and especially in Africa, where everything, or almost everything, still remains to be done.
The creation of the human, material and financial resources to ensure the survival of this ill-treated continent is an urgent necessity if the women and men who inhabit it are to have an environment that favours their moral, physical, cultural and spiritual development.
On the threshold of this third millennium, Africa truly seems a ravaged land. I say land for the symbolic weight this word carries when, eliminating frontiers and cultural diversity, Africans evoke the motherland, with the strong emotional bond like an umbilical cord shaping the relationship between mother and child. In this relationship of communion, the land is perceived subjectively. It is personified, adored. It is present, and distils in the hearts of its children the wisdom of the good times and the bad.
For bad times there surely are. At this beginning of the third millennium the continent is giving dangerously beneath the thousand and one burdens placed on it. The desolate spectacle of its misery is presented every day around the world, on television or in the other media.
The images speak for themselves: images of a natural environment devastated by natural disasters which the men and women are helpless to confront because of the lack of material resources, expert advice and logistic means: images of famished faces and silhouettes tortured to an indecent extent by poverty and disease: images of entire peoples humiliated, oppressed, their means of subsistence plundered by the madness of corrupt and bloody dictators: images of the genocide in Rwanda, in Burundi, in Sierra Leone: images of the wars in the Congo, in Eritrea, in Angola: images of the horror in Algeria: images of the *coups d'état*... And this list is by no means exhaustive, and the latest news (the massacres between religious groups in Kaduna, Nigeria) does little to excite optimism.
However... In the sixties, the poet and president Léopold Sedar Senghor managed to confer a mythical dimension on the coming of the year 2000, which took firm root in the hearts of the people of Senegal, and of other Africans, who were still drunk on the euphoria of recently won independence. It was, above all else, the dream of a radiant future that they shared. The year 2000 came to symbolise an era of light, the

marvellous moment when the flower of our hopes was to burst into bloom, with dignity rediscovered for Africa and her children; the entry into the club of wealthy, developed and free nations.
A beautiful dream! And so powerful that Sallô Dièye, a singer from Saint-Louis, Senegal, paraded his saxophone up and down the country to raise his hymn to hope *L'an 2000 Atum Teranga laa* (The year 2000 will be the year of happiness). His warm and moving voice vibrated in the hearts of all those who heard him and evoked the forthcoming radiant universe a paradise of abundance, of brilliant lights, of skyscrapers, in short, of all that which makes Paris the essence of magnificence in the minds of Africans, especially French-speaking Africans.
Forty years on, the awakening has been more than brutal. Given that everything can be said in song, Alpha Blondy, the popular singing star from the Ivory Coast, goes straight to the point: "The enemy of the Africans, are the Africans". Unfortunately, he is right. Africa has everything it needs to develop, at least in terms of natural resources, but the energies that could have transformed this potential into real tangible benefits for the population have been consumed by dictatorships, wars, genocide, and the brain drain which has naturally followed.
From the dream of Senghor to the heartfelt cry of Alpha Blondy, Africa offers the world the desolate image of a giant stumbling backwards, a giant who blindly turns his back on the demands of the future, without which no nation today would be able to survive. These requirements are peace, yet Africa is at war; freedom, yet here intolerance and exclusion prosper; the passion for overcoming difficulties, yet we are paralysed by our lack of belief in our ability to face the challenge of surviving with dignity just as other nations have done, nations that, like us, had nothing more than their brain, their brawn and their universe.
It is true that Africa has, throughout her long history, suffered grave injuries that have slowed her development. The denigrating treatment she has been subjected to has bled her dry, humiliated her. The withdrawal into herself around archaic values has delayed her joining the path of modernity, the only way that any people, in accordance with their aspirations, their culture and their necessities, can adapt to the passage of time, which necessarily evolves. As evolution is a law of nature –for

it is inscribed in the very order of things– every static or regressive positioning must lead to disaster, to extinction.
Colonisation, in its most positive aspects, opened doors that offered numerous Africans access to modern knowledge and allowed them to become acquainted with other values: those that consecrate individual freedom, for example. However, the colonial system was no bed of roses. There was violence, racism and oppression, humiliation and plundering. In short, behaviours that did nothing but drain the enthusiasm that is vital to the spirit of creativity and to the maintaining of grand ambitions.
However, these episodes in our history should not condemn us to lethargy and dependence. We must reject the mentality that demands assistance indefinitely. Having gained independence, all Africans expected happiness. Today, on the threshold of the third millennium, Africa has experienced a dangerous regression and has allowed itself to be overtaken by emerging countries like Korea which, in 1960, were far, far behind, economically speaking. Unemployment, poverty, corruption and the failure of the education system are debilitating African society to the extent of giving rise to a feeling of desperation amongst many Africans who are now convinced that there is nothing to be done.
"Africa is finished", they say. And people believe they should flee to save themselves, as if they were leaping from a sinking ship, and this leads to other dramas, other humiliations.
It is obvious, therefore, that there are emergencies in Africa. For Africans, facing up to them is a sacred responsibility. In my view, the first of these emergencies is psychological in nature: we must learn to trust ourselves, to trust in our capacities, in our intelligence, in our ability to construct Africa, just as others have done in the lands in which they were born. Above all else, we must keep in mind an overriding duty: we must construct a dignified Africa. Any other attitude would be dangerous. Above all morally, for it would be a way of confirming the idea of a supposed congenital incapacity, of an irredeemable handicap.
In the sixties, René Dumont published a book entitled *L'Afrique noire est mal partie* (Black Africa has started badly). In it, he revealed errors in the policies for the development of the continent, the mismatch between the methods chosen and the socio-cultural realities of the country. The book

provoked an outcry since numerous African intellectuals saw nothing in it but a paternalist reaction. Yet today we can state categorically that Africa started badly. Why?

> Because no account has been taken of socio-cultural particularities in the definition and implementation of development policies. To give just one absurd example, some very expensive machinery has not stood up to the rigours of the climate. But it has to be paid for. The external debt, about which so much is heard nowadays, can be explained, in part, by situations such as this.

> The Africans had only been prepared for the hand-over of political power. The new African states continued to be economically, financially and technically dependent. For this reason, even today, almost all African countries depend economically on the West and can only survive thanks to financial aid from international organisations.

A whole string of examples could be given. All of them would demonstrate that the basic dilemma of Africa is a problem of choice, of methods, of a firm commitment to an ideal.
Every nation negotiates its changes of direction and prepares its mutations with balance and harmony in view. To err in these changes of direction often means plunging into chaos. The current situation in Africa is due in large part to the fact that the Africans –those who take the decisions– have failed to commit all their enthusiasm, all their passion, all their creativity to a single magnificent project: that of saving Africa in order to save themselves. Often they have preferred only to save themselves forgetting that umbilical bond that makes sense of every life. When we come to realise the need to advance with our stock of culture always available for us to refer to, enriched by the honour that our very existence implies, then will we step out on the path of hope. Without doubt the path will be long, lasting well into the third millennium, but it will be glorious. I believe in it because the land is so beautiful and so generous, and because, as the Wolof proverb so aptly puts it, "Mankind is [still] the remedy for Mankind".

Dakar, 2 May 2000

Antjie Krog

Not the colour of the skin, but the colour of the heart. An African essay

Spin the globe in space. And see us.
Here on this continent drifting like a big black plundered heart. Morose and mumbling.
Sometimes nothing more than a lost continent on which lost figures commit lost deeds of forlorn trust. Sometimes a big black angry heart where thousands die daily into soundless bone-raking brooms.
Now and then the heart splays out its clogged and crooked valves, rig its full sails to the wind and anvigate the earth in celebration of a vision of what we could be. So soft, so humanly skinned, so profoundly light and kind as soul. So caring as to surpass all understanding.
This is us. Us of the African continent.
(But who am I to say? When does a settler become native? When does white become black? The obsession of my country has always been race. Racism. Affliction of colour. Black and white. Racialisation, the deep purulent wound of South Africa. The overtone, the undertone, the leading tone of every bristling fibre. Colour, or the absence of it).

Nescafé instant coffee has cracked the West-African market. This is a fact. Whether you order *Café Latte* in Dakar, Abidjan or Bamako, or whether you find yourself in total isolation in the Sahara, everywhere a neat satchel of instant Nescafé coffee would be at your disposal. Nescafé Instant coffee can become the only constant factor on your journey. In the cities foamy wilk will be offered on which you can scatter Nescafé granules. Deeper into the rural areas the milk change, from pasteurised to raw to goat, always, always slightly grained with sand. I even had Nescafé with a suspicious brand of mother's milk at one stopover. The worst coffee experiences were at places without instant milk or electricity. Though I must admit, emptying a satchel of granules on your tongue early in the morning provides its own kind of delight.

We are nine African poets. We start our journey on the slave island of Gorée and we travel by bus, by train, by boat to Timbouctou, the city burdened by conflicting Legends.
The beginning is the door on the island of Gorée: the place of no return. Words step back through the door, says Senegalese poet Thierno Seydo

Sall. We pick up the words. We carry them back over the threshold. We remember those whose bodies were turned in one direction and their souls to another, says Were Were Liking from Cameroon. We've come back to find the equilibrium between the body and the direction of the longing. That is the point were the dance begins.

Malian poet in billowing dress, Albecaye Ousmane Kounta, admonishes: the griot is the double shadow of the people, it is the word and the journey of the word; we are but birds coming from all over Africa to see the word passing, to eat the word, to transform sword to word, to forge the collective word.

(President Nelson Mandela made reconciliation his mission. Our new President, Thabo Mbeki, has another mission: we have to succeed.

We simply have to succeed. Whereby he means that the South African government has to establish the kind of black government which allow every citizen to lead a dignified life.

A greater dream no-one can have.

South Africa has been cut off from Africa for nearly fifty years. Apart from the exiles, South Africans, black, white, coloured, from whatever origin, had no easy access to Africa except to frightening documentaries depicting a continent falling from chaos into ruins; the latest coup by the latest overweight dictator with sunglasses and a wailing cavalcade.

Whenever Africa hit the headlines, during the long Apartheid years, it reached us via the international media. We internalised our continent through the eyes of Europeans and whites. When we called ourselves African in the past, most of us hardly had a clue what we were saying. When we stretched our hands emotionally to "our brothers and sisters in Africa", most of us were embracing an abstraction. Of course there were exceptions. And the exception of literature. But the media, education, censureship, poverty and boycotts, saw to it that we were yearning to be part of a continent we hardly knew.

We assumed everybody was black and the same and for us. That an Eastern Cape Xhosa could feel profundly uncomfortable in a French speaking muslim country or that an Afrikaner could feel comfortable with a fellow Christian Egyptian, never entered our minds).

It's not only the word, but the journey of the word. The trace of the word. The colour of that trace. It's also to journey towards the word and to travel with open eyes:

African lovesong 1

Neither the moist intimacy of your eyelids fragrant as fennel
nor the violence of your body held back behind mists
nor what emerges from ruins as your life
has such slender mercy
as to see you breathe

I Keep seeing you for the first time
holding time and again
for the briefest of times

you with the breast of baobab and quiver
quava and scabs of moon
you with your haughty griefs
staining every human hollow mercury blue with heat

will we?
survive each other

even if the sun culls the cities
the state simmers a scum of words
we stuff our hearts blatantly with sky
and the fireworks of finches
even if my eyes ride rags to the horizon
noon rides the rocks blind and bareback
the mountain sparks conspiracies against the stars

we'll survive each other

do see me
at times
for the first time

Above the make shift stage in Tambacounda the moon slips into full.

We cross the border from Senegal to Mali at midday. We wait hour at customs in the dreariest of places. People just sit in the heat. Not sitting and fanning themselves, or sitting reading, or sitting talking, or sitting listening to a radio, or sitting working. Simply sitting, with clear clean eyes as if one can walk through them.
A rat is decomposing next to where we buy bread, its red thigh maggoty. A veil of files rises from the counter. Not the heart of darkness at all, but the heart of fuckall perhaps...
The border post with its waiting people becomes over time and heat the heart of desperation. In *Le Vestibule de la Parole*, we take off our shoes and sit on carpets.
We are the Guardians of Memory, say the griots. We live by the daily bread of the word. We eat the daily word we utter. We carry the whole history of the Sudan in our mouths. The word in itself is a culture of grace. We are the carpenters of memory, the human dignity of the word, the nobility of the word.
We are the Masters –not of creation, but of the transmission of the soul.

What West Africa, and most of the rest of the continent for that matter, has not cracked, is the boring knowledge of sewage systems and airconditioners. How a population is able to produce the most complex, majestic and awe-inspiring architecture, music, literature and art, while not being able to implement a long drop is a question begging an answer. Perhaps the time has come for an energetic NGO dealing in shit disposal and cool air. Hotels are reasonably available in Senegal and Mali. All of them have fans, most of them airconditioners (few of any of these work and mostly look as if being salvaged from a second World War submarine). It transpires that there are various airconditioner stages: it cannot work at all as a rust lump, it can vibrate out of the wall after being switched on, it can sound like a knife being thrown into a propeller every 39 seconds, it can blow only hot air, it can work perfectly while drenching your room overnight, leaving you with wet suitcases and feet.

(Everywhere there are signs that the new ruling middleclass in South Africa share the white angst that the country's roads, sewage, city conditions will "fall back" to what has been termed Third World standards.

What lingers in the mind after African sports events and conferences, is the energetic shopping done by fellow Africans in South Africa's shopping malls. We are shown television footage with taxi's and buses loaded to the brim with microwaves, fans, irons, fridges, televisión sets, radios... They have visited the consumer mecca of Africa).
The name of Tombouctou was already heard outside Africa before medieval times and even then already linked to wealth. In 1324 a caravan of Mansa Musa, the Emperor of Mali, stopped in Cairo on its way to Mecca. It was a caravan unequalled by anything seen in Egypt before. The traders from other parts of the world in Cairo gasped at the display of wealth in the size of the caravan, the spectacular cloghes and jewellery, the harnesses of the camels and cattle and of course the gold. This all came from Tombouctou.
Since then and until the 14th and 15th centuries the name Tombouctou haunted the imagination of the West. It was the essence of all mystery, all secrets, it became the word for distance and isolation beyond experience: bounded on the one hand by an ocean of sand where thousands of camels disappeared in storms, their bones linig the route from oasis to oasis; on the other side, the steaming lakes and marshes which became known as the White Man's Grave.

But there is of course the hotel in Mopti –the last stop for convoys of trucks before they take on the desert. The hotel is exquisitely decorated, has no menú, but provides salad, vegetables and spaghetti! It is run by a Lebanese couple not older than thirty. I ask the proprietor: how do you do it? Mopti is hundreds of kilometers of unpassable roads from anywhere. He explains. There are old trade routes right through Africa established through the centuries by Lebanese, Indians and Arab traders. Knowing these routes, one can travel right across Africa, finding food and lodging everywhere. His family had links with one of the stopovers in Senegal. After the latest destruction in Lebanon, he married his wife and left for Africa. He studied the routes, found some gaps, started working in Mopti and in the end bought the hotel where he recently erected a second one. He sent for the rest of his family in Beirut but first had them trained: the one brother an airconditioning expert, the other an electrician, the brother in law a plumber. The wives look after a vegetable and fruit garden as well as a chicken run. They take a four by four once a month to Bamako, the capitol of Mali, to buy essentials. Once a year two brothers fly to France to buy spare parts and other equipment. His children are still small, but he will install one of his aunts in Dakar near a private school catering for the personel of the French Embassy.

Protected like a jewel by nature was Tombouctou –place of learning, place of peace, place of culture, place of exotic sophistication, but above all dreamplace of unlimited wealth. Tombouctou, a place unlike any other. Through the centuries the wealth of Tombouctou was invariably given in loving detail, but the position of the place on a map remained vague. It took a long time before the explorers could place Tombouctou next to the untraceable route of the Níger.
Yet many knew the name, tecause Tombouctou became part of the written record when Leo Africanus wrote in 1526:

"The rich king of Tombuto hath many plates and sceptres of gold, some whereof weigh 1,300 pounds. And he keeps a magnificent and well-furnished court... here are a great store of doctors, judges, priests, and other learned men, that are bountifully maintained at the king's expense. ... And hither are brought diverse manuscripts or written books out of Barbarie, which are sold for more money than any other merchandise. The coin of Tombuto is of gold without any stamp or superscription".
A company formed in London in 1618 to establish trade with Timbouctou described it as the place where: "... roofs of houses (were) covered with plates of gold, bottoms of rivers glistened with the precious metal and the mountains had only to be excavated to yield a profusion of the metallic treasure".

Early in the 19th century WM Thackeray gave voice to the Western dream of Tombouctou:

In Africa (a quarter of the world)
Men's skins are black, their hair is crisp and curled;
And somewhere there, unknown to public view,
A mighty city lies, called Tombouctou.

In the same year Alfred Tennison won a prize at Cambridge with his poem *Timbuctu* which describes the Niger drying up in the desert:

Lo! How he passeth by
And gulfs himself in sands as not enduring
To carry through the world tose waves, which bore
The reflex of my City in their depths

That Tombouctou was also a place of enviable learning was seldom mentioned. The university was thought to be one of the great centres of Islamic culture. It was also said that the Greek and Latin texts would have to be corrected one day against the manuscripts preserved there.
But the myth of wealth was so powerful that when the first Westerner arrived in Tombouctou, he dared not admit his disappointment. It was only after successive explorers described Tombouctou as nothing more than a dreary mud village run by murderous Muslims, that the West gave up its dream of becoming rich on Africa's gold. By then, however, the slave trade provided them with "black gold".

Indeed, white, red-crusted tensed-up hattet tourstis in expensive four by fours is a reasonably common sight in West Africa. Mostly from France, Belgium and Holland. Geared to the teeth for any break down in "civilisation" they clasped their pale energetic children firmly by the arms for an airconditioned picnic in the back of a four by four, while daddy in a broadrimmed navy hat inspects the tyres.

(But the ignorance of isolation is also present in the continent about us. Black people in West Africa tell me: South African blacks are not African, too much of you whites have rubbed off on them. They are greedy and selfish and arrogant like whites. And Mbeki's Renaissance? Bah! He's trying to buy himself an African suit, he, the most western of them all. I hear that in Nigeria they call us little America. I hear they warn each other that South Africa plays a key role in globalisation, a synonym for neo-colonisation of Africa. They say South Africa will have to come into step with the continent, not they with us).

Over 2,000 people gather in the square in front fo the Sankore mosque –once the famous university of Tombouctou where 25,000 people received knowledge each by imminent now forgotten erudites. For more than four hours people listen, participate and cheer a fusion of poets, griots and musicians in a language tapestry of French, Arabic, English, Afrikaans, Wolof, Tamashek, Songhai, Shona and even Dutch.

With griots and imams we explore the language of Tombouctou, the city of two pasts: the Western myth and the African reality; greed and wisdom. For centuries Tombouctou was the focal point of two diverging natures: the West's dream that Tombouctou in the place of ultimate wealth; the African memory of the seat of all knowledge, wisdom and the miracles of Saints.

At the fringe of the crowd a Nomad on a fiery white horse is looking on. A flock of goats gaze away down one of the alleys. A special convoy has turned up: a group of Arabic teachers spread all over the desert who clubbed together for transport on hearing that the famous Egyptian poet, Zein El Abdin Fouad, is to read his work in Arabic. After his performance they rise with tears streaming down their cheeks.

African lovesong 2

do I miss him already,
–ochre one I never had?

can skin say so much
in the shades of words?

can sky slip so soft?
can sand reel so free?

I remember you with my arms
on a river of blessing and bliss

the boat drenched in blue
is heavy with heart

I miss him already
And the ochre I've had

I keep losing him
still...

In the government hotel sits a despondent French citizen. He was sent by his European NGO to come and set up sundriven wells in the desert, water is brought to the surface by sundriven equipment. The NGO will sponsor the drilling, constructing and the maintenance, but in return it wants a small amount of money to assist in the motivation and the upkeep. So this man spent a month in Timbouctou, meeting endless delegations of Tuaregs from the deepest parts of the desert. Nobody understands why they should pay. They want more wells, yes, they want easy access to it, yes, but why should they pay? He sighs: "I explained that they could plant vegetables and sell it. At the word 'vegetables' they stared at me. Vegetables? 'We eat meat and milk, perhaps dates, sometime watermelon. Who will buy vegetales from us? It takes us days to reach Timbuctu, so who will buy all these wilted things from us?' 'Well, you could sell water to the caravans passing by. But this was a big mistake on my part. One of the absolute rules of the desert is apparently that you never never refuse anybody water'." The Frenchman opens some Nescafé: "My wife will not believe I've come to this", he points at the satchel instan cofee and shudders.

(South Africans feel that the only important debate, the real debate in our country is one of race, the debate between black and white. Every election, every political crisis, every controversy cons South Africans into thinking the most important and decisive debate in Africa is the one between black and white.
Of course it is a very important debate. Of course the way in which black and white manage to live together, share, reconcile and deal with ethnic tensions is important for the well being of South Africa. But I believe that is not the decisive debate of the country nor of the continent.
The crucial debate of Africa is the one about power relations.

Should one have opposition based on ethnicity, or principle? What is the use of opposition if it is ethnic, Yuveri Museveni of Uganda once asked, pointing to the continent's inability to distinguish between ethnicity and opposition. A country ought to have values which are cutting across all divides, human values for everybody. Opposition should point out how these values are being trampled on or could be put in place more effectively.
As in most African countries, opposition in South Africa is mainly ethnic in origin fighting for privileges. Ethnic opposition changes the focus of governments from accountability to coopting or fighting minorities.
Is Africa redefining the concept of opposition? Redefining the power balance in the concept democracy? Opposition? Coup? Corruption? Colonialisation? Globalisation?
That is the debate.
The relationship between the poor and the elite, the politicians and the population, the accountability of those in power and those without, the ruler and the ruled. Those who have the power to the resources and those who are completely without it. Those who tap the electricity cables and she walking past it with firewood on her head. Those who design the colossal dam wall and she carrying a bucket of water. He who write the speeches for the power wielders and the little girl with wild plaits and the brave stalk of neck singing her own song along the way.
I believe that the moment a country step into that debate, the view of white, or black, or Arab, or Egyptian, or Portugese, francophone or anglophone, mulatto, or muslim, or christian, Indian or Catholic, European or African, Hutu or Tutsi, west or east African, Sub-Sahara or Middle East Africa will find a functional place within a bigger and crucial context of the wellbeing of this continent. The absence of this debate about power relations between the politicians and the populace, distorts the focus of many countries into an exclusive racial or ethnic one).
The afternoon before we leave Tombouctou we are invited by the Tuaregs for tea in the desert. The invitation came from the mayor of Arouane.
We leave the sultry government hotel in four-by-fours under the vigilant eye of the man with the most exquisite business card in the world: "Mohamed Halice Ahassane, Saharan Guide".

It is far. After a while the young drivers in blue cloth start racing one another with cheerful abondon through the dunes. We hang on mostly from the roof, while they goad and yell through open windows. In dashing circles of reeling sand, they stop under a dune and it's like arriving on a movie set. Spread over the sand are large colourful carpets edged by low stuffed couches. The sun is setting like a red moon over the lips of dunes. The Tuaregs serve us small glasses of sweet tea. With dusk comes the poetry.

Arabic poetry

Oh the woman with the whitest eyes. She folded a cloth around her breasts. Whether she said, "Be greeted" or "Come in", I cannot remember. I was lost. May Allah grant that she becomes mine or I will lose my mind.

The nomads slap their colleague on the shoulder. The Egyptian poet recites some fo the first desert poetry from pre-Islamic times: the moon, the dunes, the sound of horses, I live by them.

The head of the Tuareg community recites poetry of the revolution: even if they break my pen, my words take fire; even if they destroy my horses and camels, I will haunt their wrists, even if they take my last breath, I will keep scorching their necks.

"I don't think, I sing", says the poet from Tunis, Amina Saïd. "I am the poet of silence. I am the poet of the journey, the vagabond of the word", says Chrikure Chirikure of Zimbabwe in Shona.
Poetry is always busy with light, glowing from the inside. Poetry is a ritual of sound draped over light. So we can live fully in this world and access our complete soul, say I.

Buchi Emecheta

New dawn

At the beginning of the last millennium, many African countries were still being "carved out" and colonised by the leading countries of the West. At the end of it, an air of freedom wafted around these formerly colonised places. During the time between, we had room to grow, room to experiment and space to make our own mistakes.

At the moment however, some countries are like children. Children who would not let go of their parent's apron strings. They cling to the parents for protection, they blame the parents for past mistakes, and hold them responsible for the present and without doubt for the future. Some parts of Africa refuse to grow up.

The early colonization was so total, that men went to war to fight for the colonial masters. The general impresión was that the natives would gain independence after the wars. The freedom was given after further struggles in which some African leaders were imprisoned and others lost their lives. Some geographical boundaries were re-drawn, colonised names dropped in favour of native original ones. Like a slave abandoning his slave name and choosing a meaningful one. Thes was a period of hope, a time of great euphoria.

As hope soared during the celebrations, there were bright laughing young people sauntering in front of new gleaming universities. Beatiful roads wer planned and built. In Nigeria, the most populous country in black Africa, rich oil began to flow. Some of the wealth was spent in fighting to free other African countries still in colonial bondage. Oil money was spent in funding the great Black Arts Festival of 1977.

From my part of Africa, the use of the English language was and still is of great help. As children, we were banned from speaking our emotional language in schools. Our instructors thought our emotional tongue would compromise our intonation. As a result, our leaders and educators acquired the English language of the book. We are always mindful of the intricate grammar, but for many of us, the voice is still very much African. The language is still serving us well. It shoud. We did not ask to be colonised. The language was forced on us. And luckily, now, it does not just serve the British Empire, nor just the needs of the original English, it serves the needs of many people whose understanding and imagination overlap tribal and national boundaries –the Commonwealth and of course, the Americans. At first this free gift was regarded as the language of our enslavement. Now it is one of the tools of our freedom. Sometimes one wonders whether if the powers that would have been less keen in teaching it to us. Now a Nigerian tribal chief can hold a meaningful conversation with an African American, with an Indian, and even with his fellow Nigerian. Nigeria alone has more promotes understanding even within the country.

After independence, power was entrusted into the hands of leaders most glib and flamboyant in the language. It became the language of success, and the language of the politicians. The same was the case of those colonised by the French, the Germans, the Italians, and the Belgiums. Things worked well for a little while. During which time the colonial masters had time to congratulate themselves on work well done. Africans were handed their freedom. Freedom to rule themselves in the language of their departing masters. But and a very big but, the departing colonisers kept close control of trade, industries and growth. This was cleverly achieved in the form of loans. Our leaders were lured to see the Western gleaming cities, and of course they liked what they saw. The loans were to hasten the development of African tribal comunities into the concrete and faceless jungle of the Western cities. We are atill paying the interest on those loans. As for repaying the capital, that will apeen only when God send this world into its Armageddon! As a result, some African countries will always be slaves to the end of time. The slave yoke is still around their necks, and the slave chain tightly hindering their ankle of progress.

But the developing world leaders do not or cannot see it that way. How can a country grow when the greater part of its resources is already spent before it is earned? The situation attract Western trained politicians, glib and cleber in the use of the language or success –that of their departed colonial masters. And of course like their heroes, they too would like

to line their pockets, and if the seat becomes too hot, to disappear as political asylumist. They make sure though, that a stack of their country's wealth is resting in one of the banks of their friendly nations.
For the ordinary person, the honeymoon was long over. Things began to fall apart. The laughing students in front of those gleaming universities, became bitter youths in tattered shirts. Some universties cannot even afford desks for their students. In a leading Nigerian University where I taught for a while, young men and women had to carry their chairs and desks from their over crowded romos on campus. The hospitals cannot buy adquate medicine for the sick. No running water, and electricity was temperamental and irregular. Sometimes one wonders whether a youngstee, growing up in a big city like Lagos, Nigeria, in the fifties and sixties was not better off than another living near the end of the last millennium. At least for the former, there was running water in the street taps.
Politicians start blaming each other. Naive students blame the colonisers. "If we had not been colonised, if we had not been enslaved, if we had not borrewed so much, if only the oil would flow more...".
All these if onlys brought out the army. The underpaid and underclass soldiers tasted wealth and power. They refused to go back to the barracks. Some of their colonels and Brigodiers promised to go back to the barrcacks as soon as there was peace. Peace did last for a short while, and the army is back again. This has been the story of many parts of Africa. If these changes were peaceful, it would not have brought so much bitterness into people's mouths. But changes from the military, to the civilian, were invariably accompanied by wars. Wars that were at first internal affairs usually escalated to attract outsiders, who wished to trade in arms. The heads of military became friendly with other "soldiers of fortune" form other parts of the world. The internal misunderstanding were then fanned until it glowed into a full fiery war, which scourde the country, burning buildings, killing the population, leaving those alive homeless refuges, crying and begging for food, form the very imperialistic masters they were happy to chase Hawai just a few decades ago.

Some people are still very hopeful for our continent. They say we have to go through all these teething periods before we find ourselves. This is a good point if we had not been living before the advent of imperialism. And how long will the teething period last, pray? Another millennium?
When will these senseless and internal wars end in Sierra Leone, in Nigeria, in Angola? And when will the world stop seeing pathetic faces of African children with their bloated stomach? And when will our leaders military and civilian stop garlanding their places abroad with the wealth stolen from their countries? And when will those friends who help in hiding their loot be brought to book and be charged with crime against humanity? The holocaust ended the lives of over six million innocent Jews, God only knows how many millions of African people are being wasted in hunger in refugee camps, in unnecessary wars in Sierra-Leone; in Liberia. No one is counting. In my part of the world, it used to be the survival of the fittest. You had to be very fit to survive the terrible passage in slave ships to the Americas in an earlier millenium. You had to be very lucky to survive the massacre of the Tutsis and the Hutsis, same people, who started slaughtering each other for no reason which a woman of Africa cannot see or undertand. Whatever is achieved after all this, it is not worth the price.
Cast your mind back and remember Biafra in Nigeria in the late sixties, when things were so bad that it was frightening even to turn on the television. Whatever caused that war is still there today, simmering under the surface. The young are still underpaid, there are still not enough jobs, the rich are getting richer, and the brain drain in Nigeria is escalating. There are 26.000 qualified medical doctors of Nigerian descent in America, maybe more, but we have stopped counting.
There are not enough independent doctors willing to stand up and be counted to warn our countries that the greatest killer of our continent is on its way. The killer is AIDS. A few years ago, I read a Nigerian paper that claimed that HIV and AIDS are white people's diseases. That it cannot be worset that Malaria. This could be so, a long time ago. But it is no longer the case. A well known misician from a respectable family

owned upt that he was dying of Aids. God will rest his scul. It then became reluctantly accepted that yes, there could be AIDS in Nigeria. At the on-set of the disease, many patientts annot afforc proper hospital fees. They visit the native medicine people who may tell them that they are being cursed by a witch. By the time they decide to go to a proper hospital, the HIV would have become full glown AIDS. And death already too close.
I witnessed the death of a distant relative dur ng my recent visit to my village. I was cautioned not to mention the wcrd "AIDS", because I have a young family. My mentioning the word "AIDS" may make it attack a member of my family. To avoid this Aids is given the name "gloria". I am not surprise to read in a London paper that probably one person in five in Nigeria my be HIV positive.
Our leaders are busy talking of slavery reparation, industr alising our country, but a dangerous death is knowking on all our doors.
And Nigeria is no where in comparison to places like Zambia, Uganda and Zimbabwe. Beautiful and healthy looking children from Zambia visited English churches in London recently, singing for money. They looked so well and so cheerful, that when we were later told that they were all orphans and with HIV, we found it difficult to believe. We could not believe that some of those bright children may never frow into adulthood. Some level headed leaders are clawing from the deep and doing what they can. This morning, I heard on the World Service that Ghana is now establishing "Condom Café", where young people whose parents refuse to accept the fact that their children are sexually active, can meet and be given free protection. Other so called Third World countries are tackling the problem themselves, through education. A child from Zambia told us in our church, that where he came form, they had on y children and their grandparents. These children have to grow quickly. Sadly some of them may not even live to be adults.
Like our fate in many parts of Africa, we lay the blame on Europeans who brought the AIDS. The Europeans on the other hand say we brought it through our monkeys, and so the argument goes on. The number of those

dying from the disease my be going down in the West, sadly it is not the same story among us, Africans.
This last millennium has been the age of freedom, the age of enlightenment. The voices of a little fraction of women are being heard outisde the home. Girls on the average stay longer in schools. At least some educated African women are being allowed to be aware of what is internationally right. And we hope the military that had been sent back to their barracks in places like Nigeria, will stay there, in the barracks.
One of the greatest achievements of this century in Africa is the death of apartheid. It was a long struggle, but it was accomplished in the end. People of different races are learning to live side by side. There is little doubt that it will continue to be like that.
Different dialogues are taking place in the Congo. There are similar talks in Liberia.
There will be more education in Africa, and with eduaction and understanding, many of the mistakes made since independence, will diminish.
Women will be able to speak out more as they gain more financial independence through more career choices. More laws are needed to root out the shackles of traditions that had been holding women of Africa back for ages.
The most important wish is that of peace. There cannot be any growth without peace.
In the 20th century had been a horrible millennium for Africa, the 21st can only be millennium of a new dawn. A time in which the power and dignity of dialogue rather than that of the guns should be rediscovered. Guns produced in the West, which seem to contain bullets specially targeted for African people.
The only hope for our continent is peace. One look at the picture of bewildered refugees milling around from place to place, tells the whole sorry story. Without peace of mind, without security, there can be no culture to celebrate.
A little example throws light on this.

In Nigeria's business capital, Lagos, budding pop stars air their new releases in local night clubs. These venues are fast closing, because people no longer feel safe to visit such places. There are too many unregulated guns in the hands of robbers roaming the streets at night. There is inadequate security for the average music lover. Hence, the music industry is suffering. To imagine a big African country without its music industry is almost unthinkable. Agreta loss to many.
More money is needed. So is more cooperation and committment. When the debts owed the West is cancelled, the money should be cancelled into the paths of peace. Not into the pockets of leaders who will only return it to the West in one form or another.
In the 20th Century, we blame others for our persistent failures, in the 21st, we should face facts and learn to blame ourselves.

Calixthe Beyala

Africa

I am always amazed as a black woman, an African woman, when because or articles or papers I am asked in good faith to talk of Africa, of its hopes, of its dreams and perspectives for the third millennium. I feel like an ebony sky asked to lighten the ebony of its own night. I travel along in the vacuum of en empty heart, but I write with the impression that I am writing to make the world understand that I have nothing to say, so I don't have to express my suffering at a world fraying away. However, as it is always necessary to seek not excitement, but a sense of foolishness, my memory goes back to my childhood where reasons for hoping vaguely emerge, for believing even if everything is confused by the build-up of my thoughts.

It was a time when we still believed in the great baptism of civilisation. We had no television, but under the starry nights the elders told us stories and passed on the remnants of ancestral memory. We didn't have any electricity in our homes and around stormy lamps we played *lido* and *songo*. We did not have any money and money had such a relative value that everyone took part in making daily life more bearable. We did not always stay off our hunger, but we fantasised about fridges to buy, cars to drive, beautiful finery that would make the Dior and other Chanel drool with envy. We did not have any medicines, but the women knew the plants that cured and soothed. We did not have running water and there, in the backwater, we frolicked in the crystal clear water, we drew it and took it home on our backs and we splashed the countryside with our young girls' laughter. Behind us, young boys with their desires, declaring their love for us by throwing bloody pork thighs at our feet: will you marry me? I love you.

And it was fine like that because we believed in love and even sex couldn't be worse than an accident. There were certainly obligations to marry to a certain person, and these arranged marriages, the adults said, were but arrangements with destiny. Some young girls overwhelmed by duty gave in; others in fear of their fragile souls fled to crossroads where they were waited for by the lovers their hearts made out. There were

still policies that spurned us, but they sent in their military to make sure we complied. They came along and outside their arms their eyes were already guns. And scared, ignorant, we would do what had to be done, without wondering whether it was good or bad. The essential thing was to stay alive and continue daydreaming of tomorrows in miasmas of stars, where being would one day reap the benefits of modernism. This wasn't good, but it wasn't so bad, for in this view for some so hellish, things seemed organised to us.
Today, in the same slum of my childhood, one does not choose, one moves on, but nobody knows where. It may be the macadam of the towns, in the forests or jungles where we go in pilgrimage, we no longer know where we might be. Electricity, water and television have entered the afflicted heart of our city, unworthy of applause. These benefits have arrived, hoisting their sails in the unawareness where we were. Our hearts leap in our chests at the display of western riches, its *Dallas* and other television leaflets that submerge us like waves and we, taken away by these inventions, forget who we were, what we are doing there. The women have forgotten the plants; the elders no longer talk about the past; the boys now know that there is no point in hunting, that the hormonal chickens from Europe are good enough too; the young girls with not so sagging breasts are so bored that they tie their loincloths to their hips and go off to sell; this is the love on the pavements of the great roads or in the halls of seedy hotels. Money, money! The money king, god of this new world. We run like the west behind it and go in all directions to achieve it. No conscience, no moral to guide us on this quest, without any hindrance other than fatality itself and the sky observes us perplexed. What is happening?, the stars seem to wonder. The blacks are becoming worldly, they are learning about coke and hotdogs, replies a mocking voice arising from the void. Isn't it great? Soon, through the universe, we will no longer know who you are, who I am or who totality is. Long live globalisation. As for policies, they turn the country to the left or the right, depending on what is prescribed by a law only their interests know. The international bodies have made them bring in democracy in order to spit out hope and vomit charity to relieve the poverty of the peoples. And since they must die as everything we see, to live two or ten years is the same in the end, then our Caesars here have

adopted banana democracies and we are today the only people to have a President democratically elected for life. What matter whether things are well done, as long as there is the illusion that they have been done. Even science makes us understand that our life is worth less still, since it is more important to find medicines that deal with certain western colds than a vaccination against the malaria that kills over three million people a year.
This happened yesterday and is still happening today as we are like grains of sand raised by the wind and falling back into vacuum as they are nothing, so what perspective for the future? I know nothing, I can do nothing, I study nothing. Some want to believe it; they set up crosses alongside the roads, others pass on their way, with nothing more. And me, without really believing, aspiring nonetheless to something, I say that we should go back on ourselves to the beginning of the story and change it, but this is not possible; I say that we should take the top of the Africans' brains, wash them, wring them to rid them of the miasmas of the false truths put forward by the media, let them discover the lost humanity in themselves and acquire the sense of what they are and the strength of what they can give to the world, but this is not possible for living is not necessarily becoming what one already is. I also say that the West must change its behaviour and learn to respect others in their identity and their culture, but this is a dream as their intentions have nothing to do with love, and as for fraternity they are light years away. I still think that the West could be a little more humble and learn that it is not the only one with knowledge and science, to give African man the chance to take part in building universal well-being, but this is like asking a king to get off the throne.
Then sometimes seated before an empty, silent sky, I know not whether I remember that an orange bears the umber of its quarters, that Africa itself must rise and project itself to less abrupt reasons in order to find the sense of the sense of its humanity.

Vina and the volte-face

When my father came in and said that he was going to turn the dead, I told him that he wasn't in his right mind. Perhaps it was because Mother died, but that was five years ago. And, as everybody knows, the one who had lost her mother was me. But nevertheless, the one who goes on and on about it is him, the adult. Because he had dreamt about forefathers and ancestors. He had talked to them. My father allowed himself little night-time conversations with the spirits; about how they had to be kept warm. How can one freeze when one is supposed to be decomposing? However, it was precisely the fact that the mummies were freezing that made my father organise a *famadihana*. To get them to leave their graves and to wrap them in new shrouds; and to do all that with a bundle of bones that are no longer even creaking. However impressive that may seem.

And, worst of all, my grandmother on my father's side was fully aware of what it was all about.

Seventy years old and heaps of dust. Perhaps rather too much dust up top. Anyway, I dare to have my doubts now when people speak of the old and the wise.

I asked my aunt Riana, my father's sister, if she couldn't teach them to live in the present and in modern society. She tended to be a woman with a practical turn of mind. But she told me that the living should pay their respects to their ancestors and their origins. And being as young as I was, she didn't have much opposition to deal with. Adults always think that my being only fifteen is sufficient argument.

Which, nevertheless, doesn't stop her trying to shut me up. Three against one, so I didn't really enter into it. And so, in all haste, we set about preparing this ceremony from another age. All the family came flocking in. The house was bursting at the seams. I knew some of the people who came, but there were lots more I had never seen before. My aunt Simone, my mother's sister, was the first to arrive. With her husband in a foul mood. They got out of their 1999 BMW. It was red. My aunt is a woman who has been successful in business. And she looks down a bit on my father, because he's not rich and hasn't always got the hang of what's being produced in Europe and America. Next came a distant relative of my father's. The first to appear in the doorway was his paunch. Then the rest of his body, dripping with thick gold chains. And one small one. He didn't seem so crazy. As for those who came in afterwards, I'd never ever seen them before. Although, according to my father, what we have here are family ties and common ancestry. I said nothing, because I wanted to show respect. I didn't really understand why it was so important to renew the ties that had been broken.

Then came the same old "hello, how are you? You haven't changed one little bit, after all these years!" Broad sardonic smiles, contemptuous pats on the back and polite little conversations. At that point it was all about everyday life.

Because afterwards, when the time came to deal with the matter of the exhumation, it was all about festivity and devastation, and allocating tasks and responsibilities. And about money. Now my aunt Simone was in her element, offering opinions, handing out orders, criticising, supervising and putting forward proposals. But she didn't ever take part herself. It was my father who did, who took careful note of everything and made sure that everything was done. I found it all very irritating, but my father just turned a blind eye.

Afterwards they all went off home to do their own thing.

Unfortunately they came back a few days later. With none of the smiles from the time before. The atmosphere was strained. And you could see from Aunt Simone's eyes that she was fuming.

My father took a long time to deal with what, according to Aunt Simone, he "should deal with", and kept people waiting. His way of dealing with anything was to say no to all the ceremonies. No! So, bring on disagreement, lack of harmony, discord and the whole scenario. Up, down, everything at once!

If this was supposed to be a *famadihana*, I would have preferred to stay well out of it. While the others were laying into him, I was nudging him to put a stop to it all. But, nonetheless, the one he listened to was Simone's husband, who made himself out to be an intellectual and was giving a lecture on the importance of organisation. And suddenly the fat, rich uncle threw into the middle of the room what, to my eyes, was an impressive bundle of notes. Then at last my father stood up.

First he turned to Aunt Simone. In very simple words he told stories about

when Aunt Simone and my mother were little girls. He said that it was my mother who, giggling and with such lovely warm eyes, had been the one to tell him them. I looked over at Aunt Simone. She was behaving nothing like the owner of a red 1999 BMW. Her husband opened his mouth, but said nothing and blinked. After that, my father collected up all the notes with a smile. I thought the whole thing was disgraceful. He gathered up a despicably huge amount of money, all the while talking to my Uncle Creso. He had always been surprised, he told him, by people who gave money only to outdo others or to show how good they were. Which wasn't uncle Creso's case. Father knew that uncle had always been hesitant about handing out princely sums of money, as long as he could stretch to it, just in order for others who were not equally wealthy to get away with paying as little as possible. He thanked him for his compassion and respect for the forefathers. Because, of course, this money was to be used as a contribution towards making the festivities even more splendid. My uncle took a fat cigar out of his pocket, lit it and puffed away at it as if he were running out of breath.
A distant relative broke the silence and pointed out with some irony that my father was probably not too sure as to exactly when the festivities and the exhumation should take place. In spite of all the money he had received. My father replied that he was prepared to go back to the diviner with him to ask the great sage to make haste to foretell the auspicious days for the kind of ceremony in question. Because it was these auspicious days that should bring the family both solemnity and the blessed times of the ancestors for many years to come. And it was only the great sage who could decide which days would be auspicious. As long as the here and now didn't present any obstacles.
Aunt Simone and the others sat round in a circle. They spoke very decisively. Now and again they would look over at my father, who didn't bat an eyelid. He even called upon Aunt Riana and my grandmother to serve tea and fritters. I was sitting in my corner, keeping my eyes warily on the enemy. Although, when my glance happened to fall on the boy, it did become somewhat more flattering. But I swear it went no further than that. After the worst of the arguments were over, they drank their tea. And now they were smiling once more. And they mentioned for the umpteenth time

that I had grown. And they all nodded and agreed and smiled, grinning from ear to ear. Nobody spoke any longer about the *famadihana*. I nudged my father and whispered in his ear:

"Why don't we talk about...?"

"Be quiet", said my father, "everything is ready now".

"Really?"

The whole family stood up and said that the time had come to leave. They all wished each other well and said their goodbyes. They all wished each other a long life. Uncle Creso promised to call on his new mobile. Grandmother smiled and replied that it was kind of him, but that we didn't have a phone. And a little peace and quiet descended on our house after aunt Riana and I had tidied everything up.

It turned out as my father had said. Everything that needed to be organised for the great ceremony was quickly resolved. The people came with shrouds of raw silk and cotton in the colours of the house. And with money in envelopes. And, what's more, with masses of things that I found far more appealing: poultry and zebu, pork and vegetables, fruit, tea and coffee, cocoa, flour and, of course, rice. And there were even cakes and sweets. The women and girls came round and helped us prepare the food. The men put benches, chairs, stools and tables out on the patio. Because everything was taking place in our house, and had to take place in our house. The family tomb was situated on my father's land, not too far from our house. The only thing that separated it from our patio was a red clay wall. It's a little strange that all this should have to happen in order for me to realise that each day I lived beside the dead. The last few days have made me realise that they do exist here, even though I cannot touch them, and I believe that they actually wish us well. But perhaps, as a result of these hectic days, when the living were laughing their heads off, they rose up in anger and tormented us.

Because a very congenial atmosphere had returned. Of course aunt Simone went on giving orders and the only thing she used her hands for was to point at us in an accusing manner. Behind her, her husband, uncle Tovo, gave lectures with long explanations on how to a job should be finished off. We all listened, and afterwards I asked Grandmother what we should do next.

Our whole house and patio had a party-like smell. Out on the patio the men had worked together hard together to light several fires. There was a good smell of eucalyptus and meat that was bubbling away in great big pots. The strong smell of pineapple overpowered the rest of the fruit, and the aromas of the garlic, thyme and parsley that had been placed on the platter competed with each other. I flitted about everywhere, lifting lids and rinsing a few dishes before putting them to one side and then tasted the sweet papaya or made sure that there was enough cinnamon for the tea.

On the morning of the second day of preparations, the only ones left were my grandmother, aunt Riana, two cousins and myself. We kept our eyes on the pots on the fire. The others had gone to the graves and I could hear them shouting and singing. They had opened the family tomb and were now taking the ancestors out. They would bring them here, to the patio of the living, and for several hours to come, ancestors and descendants would share moments of what they hoped would be joy and memories. I was... No, I didn't really know what I thought. I was discovering, learning something new and I was imbued with impressions. Now they had come on to the patio. Uncle Creso was the first and was whistling like crazy to make way for the company of *mpihira gasy*, the dancers and singers that the family had hired for this occasion. After them came all the innumerable relatives who held the ancestors aloft in their old shrouds that were in turn wrapped in new cloth. Aunt Simone was dancing in the midst of the crowd, and Uncle Tovo waddled like a duck at her side. Some of the women were shouting somewhat hysterically and were asking for a blessing for these dead ones who were now the fathers and mothers of the family. I went running up to them and was caught up in the rapture of communal joy. But I found it hard to take when I bumped into my father, whose eyes were brimming with tears.

"Listen, what's this all about?" I asked.

He smiled and patted me on the back.

"Nothing dear", he said, "nothing more than beautiful memories. At times I could just never manage to be of any use".

At that, Father pushed me away and told me to go off and play, because this was what the whole ceremony was all about, to make us aware that we were alive.

The ancestors were laid out on wooden litters. Alongside them, Aunt Simone laid all the new shrouds that had been given during the previous few days. She seemed to be saying "I am the one who has woven these ones". Prior to that Aunt Riana and I had put down some other sheets, which could not be found since we had put them away again.

Everybody bowed in veneration. All this did not last particularly long because Grandmother called us. We went back over towards her. And now a big crowd gathered. And it was time for the banquet to begin. In no time at all everyone present had a knife and a fork and a spoon in their hand and all the plates were filled to overflowing. Everyone sat wherever they liked but, of course, the place of honour went to Grandmother. Uncle Creso gave thanks to God and the ancestors for having allowed us to come together, to see how many of us there now were, and then said a few words about our duty, and asked them to bless our food and to look kindly upon our prosperity. I opened my eyes when I thought that his prayers had gone on long enough and noticed that half the gathering was also sitting there with their eyes open. Uncle Creso was just about to give a further explanation of the text when aunt Simone and the person sitting next to her at the table cried out "amen", which everyone echoed. Uncle Creso jumped and everybody sat down with their spoons in their mouths. He then did the same. The festive music commenced and we chewed away in time to it, with spoons and forks rattling on the plates and glasses clinking one against another all the way down the table. And all accompanied by peals of laughter. Never before had the rice been so aromatic, and the meat and the poultry melted in my mouth, and the fried vegetables slid down as easily as the lightest of pastries. But, at the very moment when everything was tasting great, uncle Tovo called me and asked me to bring him some more salt. I did as I was told. Then everybody leapt at the opportunity. They asked for more wine and sauce, peppers, vinaigrette, clean napkins, water and even ketchup. Aunt Riana came over and helped me to begin. We ran backwards and forwards between the kitchen and the patio to serve everything as quickly as possible, in order to get back to our places. But then along came the young man, a distant relative, wanting to lend us a hand. He helped me to hand out some clean plates and I helped him with some others. But then I heard a resounding “that's enough!” It was aunt Riana. The people there watched her sit down again. There was silence for a moment before aunt Simone was heard to say “Thank you, dear Riana, I don't know what we would have done without you all”. Uncle Creso just let out a “tee-hee-hee.” Anybody still hungry now served themselves.

The meal had finished and the men belched away, extremely satisfied with themselves. The women patted their stomachs and opened their mouths contentedly. People gathered together in small groups to chat to each other. Suddenly I found myself next to my distant relative. The laughter grew ever louder and Uncle Creso told anyone who might not have heard before how he had courted his wife. His wife, who was sitting next to him, shot him an angry and exasperated look. A relative I had never seen before told a cock-and-bull story that we had all heard before, and began to laugh long before he had reached the punch line, and we all joined in with his infectious laughter.

We got glasses out. Father and Uncle Tovo appeared with bottles of alcohol. They tipped the contents of the glasses over the ancestors and then turned to face everyone there. It seemed as if the women didn't know what they were doing there. They looked the other way and stretched out their arms, and that's how their glasses got filled. All the time, the *mpihira gasy* music formed part of our drunken orgy. Together with my distant cousin, I slipped away from my grandmother so that she could not stop me having a sip of the adults' drinks. The alcohol tasted of something unbelievable and forbidden. Aunt Riana turned out to be an ace rum drinker. Poor grandmother could do no more than shoot piercing glances at us.

Night fell extremely quickly and there we were in the darkness. The men propped each other up like brothers, to give the appearance of being well-behaved and, above all, to keep their balance. They jabbered away with stories that never ended, but whose ending everybody knew. The women held themselves altogether too upright for it to be for real. As for myself, I stayed right next to my relative from afar. Aunt Simone was standing in front of us. She kept on making friendly little gestures towards me. I reckoned that all misunderstandings had turned into total and intimate agreement. Great quantities had been drunk, according to some malicious gossip, but for my part, I think it was the meal itself that was to blame. The ancestors are not crazy when they say "wandering soul on an empty stomach".

One thing I did learn. The important thing wasn't to turn the dead and wrap them in new shrouds. It was more to do with what they could do for us, the living. We were full up and getting on extremely well with each other. And so I made it up with Aunt Simone. I know now that Aunt Riana doesn't always want to be reasonable. And I met a relative who had come an awful long way and who wasn't all that crazy. His name is Ny Aina, Life. Simple as that.

My own name is Vina. My grandmother often tells me that it is me who has to decide if it should mean Hope or Judgement. I usually reply that it is me, and not my name, that will determine my future.

Grandmother began to serve coffee and tea to put an end to the round of yawning that was gathering pace. Uncle Creso sat down in the middle of the patio. He thought that we were a bunch of wastrels who didn't know how to celebrate this kind of a party. He signalled to the musicians with his hand and began to perform authentic circus dances. His belly swayed, his legs were crossed over and his fingers darted about. I applauded and so did everyone else. And Uncle Tovo hauled both Father and Grandmother up onto the patio and Uncle Creso moved off. My two uncles stood next to the musicians and sang a song full of praise for my grandmother and my father, the hosts of the house. This house of ours, they chanted, gave off a regal air of fruit and direct descendants. I thought that this sounded a bit foolish but it is true that our whole family was really getting completely out of control. My grandmother began to dance for joy at being thanked in this way by everybody. The musicians' drums and the clapping of our hands provided her with the right rhythm. Next to her, Father looked a real clodhopper. He just nodded and looked appreciatively to left and right, and forward and backward. I thought he was stupid to carry on, but he was so happy, and I was happy for him. After a while we were all dancing like madmen, holding hands in a long line across the patio. Everyone was dashing around in time to the music, and not in time too; singing in tune, or completely out of tune; and grabbing the musicians' drums and cymbals for themselves, and playing them not too badly. But it was exactly as it ought to be. We were celebrating together, each of us had opened up our own little worlds and we had now listened to one other. I really like these little things that add a little spice to life. My body reacts to each vibration and my skin tingles and tingles all over. My grandmother often says philosophically that it is these little moments of happiness that keep you going. When I look at her, I am inclined to think that she is right.

After that, my father decided that it had become too dark outside on the patio. So we collected all the lamps and torches, and put them down here, there and everywhere. This gave a completely different atmosphere to the setting of the party. Some parts were in shadow and others were lit up. As a result, we began to behave differently. We danced less and less, and sat down closer and closer to others who wanted to chat. It's strange, this desire to talk and have someone talk to you, to listen and have someone listen to you, throughout these days. I mentioned this to my father and he whispered: "The ancestors do what they have to, they come close to the living. Because you should know that if it were not so, then we would prefer to have left them to lie in their graves". I wondered if I had understood correctly.

I left Father and went over to my grandmother. Ny Aina came with me. I put my arm around her old shoulders. "Are you tired?" She simply smiled. I put on my charming childlike tone of voice and asked her to tell us about "the olden days". A voice echoed my question. She let out a long sigh like an old actress. Ny Aina and I looked at each other and pulled faces about what we were up to. By chance, Grandmother spotted our glances and said furiously that "the olden days" were something good and, in those days, people at least had some respect. I wanted to apologise but my relative from afar muttered that it was the sort of thing that "they" always used to say, that everything was better before and that it was us

young people who were spoiling everything. Some of the adults told us to shut up. And our grandfather on our father's side began to speak of wild zebus, of treks through the forest and of hunting when they became hungry. "Did you hunt zebus with *Kalashnikovs*?" asked Ny Aina. I joined in the chorus of exclamations and laid my hands on those sitting next to me. Uncle Tovo gave me a smack and I muttered something about them probably not punching kids in the olden days. Uncle Tovo warned us that, if you didn't know what you were talking about, you should keep quiet at all times and in all situations. You should just keep to the subject of your own kids. He, on the other hand, knew perfectly well, because he had read about it, that zebus were being hunted to such an extent that they were within a whisker of being exterminated. My Aunt Simone wondered out loud "My dear, who is it that should be exterminated?" My uncle swallowed hard and replied "The zebus, of course!" He leapt to his feet in one bound and, with a display of enormous indignation, stamped his foot on the ground and uttered the most wonderful "moo!" you've ever heard. Ny Aina and I shouted "More, more, off with the zebu!" Other voices joined in and, along with us, improvised a war chant, forming a circle around the "zebu", and pushed him into a corner. The powerful animal bellowed desperately and put up a fight for as long as he could. What a fantastic night.
Grandmother and Aunt Riana applauded our heroic deed. Aunt Simone thought it looked clever but didn't serve any real purpose. I called out:

"Uncle Tovo, I just love you as a zebu!"

I could see that my preferences were not particularly popular.

Then Aunt Riana said "Shall we go and dig around in our treasure trove of stories?"

"Yes! Let's take a look and get nostalgic about our ancestors!"

"And nobody shall have the right to decide what is a story and what is the truth!"

"Exactly! What's important is that we can wrap ourselves in our dreams!"

"Excellent." said Uncle Creso, getting to his feet before continuing, "Look at me –I am the salt of the West and the sweet honey of the East. Try it, my little ones, and you will find out how deliciously sweet it is."

Ny Aina burst out laughing and dug his elbow into my side. My uncle's wife said that my uncle was a sex maniac and threatened him with all manner of divine curses. My uncle explained yet again to his wife that she didn't have a clue, and that this was how young men used to court young women in the olden days.

"Well then, let some others have a go, you've done your bit as a rooster! We've got to draw the line somewhere with all these dreams!"

I tried to find out from all the others if this was really the way to declare your love. It wasn't a good idea. A young girl in the family asked me if I wouldn't like to have a little bit of poetry in my life. I didn't know exactly what I was supposed to say in reply. Ny Aina wondered aloud what you had to do now to get close to someone. Nobody answered him. Obviously this problem was far from being resolved. Then I asked Grandmother if she had ever really been in love, and how she had found that love. She declared shyly that it had nothing to do with anybody else. One woman in the family, listening to this exchange, detected tricks and dangerous games. And another one added: "Ho, ho, you little rascals!" Grandmother shouted that, in her time, all young people who were in love got properly married straight away, and didn't go round shamelessly living it up, and, least of all, without anybody's blessing. Another woman in the family wondered what one had to do to get to know someone else a bit better. Aunt Simone burst out laughing: "They could write to each other, along the lines of: 'I am writing to you, my beloved, beneath the blue sky of laryo, with my golden pen'". One relative, with her eyes twinkling, recalled that this was more or less how people used to write to each other: "You are not here, my love, and I understand why." What she meant by this is that when you miss one particular person, the world is empty. Another woman said: "inuendo..., because it was during the colonial period when French poets were read". And the women began to laugh and laugh. They probably had something else in mind.

Ny Aina stood up and looked at me with his hand on his heart and recited "You are my interplanetary rocket, a satellite in my universe".
My father interrupted him and asked whether he had really sat his baccalaureate. Grandmother declared that she thought the little pipsqueak was actually talking seriously. I was on the point of disagreeing, but a relative wondered out loud how one should really dress for a truly fine wedding. Grandmother replied that one thing was for sure, you didn't go in disguise. Another woman asked if it was her trousers that were attracting so many glances. And then several of the men said that, if the truth be known, they preferred skirts and, even better, wraparounds that overlapped just slightly. And long hair would be the icing on the cake. "You poor wretches!" a relative with short hair shouted. She stood up and started to sing:

I am a lonely plant that grows
high up on Ankaratra,
The wind must whistle over me
But I stand upright.
Oranges when the time is right
And sugarcane in Spring.
He who knows not who I am
Will be forever sorry.

After that, this modern woman with words of days gone by went off with her hips swaying like mad. "What a cheek!" somebody muttered. But many of the women applauded and went out after her. They said they were planning a bit of girls' talk, and that the "kings of the phallus" should keep themselves well hidden. The men shrugged their shoulders and reckoned that they might as well have a game of cards or play dominoes. The youngest among them offered to sing. Songs of peaceful nights of long ago rose into the night sky.
I felt good. Happy both in body and spirit. Thanks to all the ancestors! Thanks for a *famadihana* like this, this journey from and between a present and a past, and these brief moments of questioning.
I suggested to Ny Aina that just the two of us should say goodnight to the mummies. Straight away he decided to come along with me. In the

special place reserved for the ancestors I introduced him to my great-grandfather on my father's side, a chatterbox, or so it was said. And his wife, my great-grandmother, who died at the same time as him. I have come to realise that I was extremely fond of her. Then a shrill little voice replied that it was a pity. It was my great-grandmother. The shameless spectre, clothed in natural ochre rags, butted into the conversation between Ny Aina and myself.
I asked what business it was of hers. Because I preferred to have something to go by. At school they spoke of role models and learning by rote, because those who came before us "were good". How do we handle that? She sighed deeply to show me that she had now had more than enough of me. Would I, at my age, and in the year 2000, still drag up the past once again? She scratched away at her arms furiously. This raised a little cloud of dust, and I couldn't help mentioning it. "It's just the earth", she said, "you have to let it impregnate you until you die, and then it follows you to the grave". And she began to hum:

Dream, earth, and open your door,
Dream, earth, and let live,
Dream, earth, and give sustenance.

I kept quiet. My great-grandmother laughed silently to herself. "Don't dwell on it any longer", she joked, "I simply tried to ask you to listen to and live with your ancestors, with all your heart and not with your head. It is not us who decide on prohibitions and pretexts. We are worth more than that. And so are the living. And now, my little friend, it is your turn to play, for us the game is over. May happiness go with you, for happiness is the only thing you should show us".

"Listen", cried Ny Aina, Life "are you still with me?"

I smiled at him, took his hand and once more we thanked the ancestors for donning their new shrouds, and laid them where they were to remain. It was time for us, the living, to get on with our daily life again. With our ancestors like a pale background and a land that is deeply buried within us.

Donato Ndongo-Bidyogo

Africa at the end of the millennium

For an African, it is difficult to feel optimistic about the prospects for our continent at the turn of the millennium. The most widespread feeling amongst Africans right now is that of frustration, a frustration that grows out of the poverty that corrodes us, that prevents us from living a normal life that is minimally dignified. Dominating this is the conviction that we are not in control of our own lives, that to survive in this global world we depend on the decisions, and the goodwill, of others. For we have been stripped of that most precious of human attributes, the capacity to take charge of our own lives, basic in retaining one's self-esteem. As the century turns, every African bears within their soul the stigma of failure, an enormous void in their life, for the signs could not be worse, and the future is a black hole in which no light can be discerned. The underdevelopment of our countries is reaching apocalyptic levels, in a world where, in general, the wealth and welfare of nations is growing.

But what is underdevelopment? To speak of this we cannot only deal in abstract terms, nor restrict ourselves to macro-economics. Behind the bald statistics lies the suffering of millions of people, each one with their own life, plans and dreams. They are real people, with relatives, with friends. First, then, we should ask ourselves how we have reached this situation, the reality of our here and now. How is it that in the last decade the life expectancy of a black African has fallen from 60 to 50 years, while in other parts of the world it has risen to 80 or 85? Are we Africans so different from the rest of humanity that we actually like living in filth, ankle deep in sewage and rubbish, an image that can be found in any one of our cities, in the neighbourhoods not occupied by the whites and those of the local classes who benefit from the political regime?

What is happening to us, the Africans, that is causing us to die from diseases that in the rest of the world are no longer fatal? What is it that is causing infant and neo-natal mortality to increase in our countries? That we continue to live without the basic facilities that are taken for granted elsewhere, like running water or electricity? Why do the per capita incomes of the African countries remain so paltry, and our economies fail to take off, despite increasing global wealth and the over-exploitation of our raw materials? How can we explain that, in the 21st century, after fourty years during which many countries have gained independence, 43% of the

children in sub-Saharan Africa do not go to school, and that this figure, far from diminishing, is in fact increasing? According to the international aid agency, Oxfam, in 2015 three quarters of all children who do not attend school will be black Africans. How is it possible to understand that of the 2.2 million people who died from AIDS in 1998, 1.8 million were African, and of those, half a million were children? This disease, according to the figures of the United Nations AIDS organisation, has affected thirty four million black Africans, of whom 11.5 million have already died. According to the information given by experts at the 9th International Conference on AIDS in Africa, attended by five thousand people in September 1999 in Lusaka, Zambia, this illness alone has cut life expectancy by twenty five years in countries such as the Ivory Coast, where it kills one teacher every day. But apart from the AIDS pandemic, our countries are also gravely affected by epidemics such as haemorrhagic fever, poliomyelitis, meningitis, hepatitis, cholera, bubonic plague, yellow fever, and of course, the most widespread of all, paludism or malaria. Naturally, these diseases have repercussions not only in the health of those who are infected but also in the economy of the countries, and thus in the quality of life of those who are healthy. For example, the impact of AIDS is reducing the productivity of African companies since there are many people who are too ill to go to work. The middle class, the driving force behind economic development in other parts of the world, is being decimated in our continent.
I could go on like this for some time, dissecting the economic and social situation in Africa as a whole, and in each country, but perhaps one final example will serve to illustrate the situation. Since 1974, the number of people living in poverty in the world has doubled. The Secretary General of the United Nations, Kofi Annan, denounced this fact in July last year in his opening address to the annual session of the Economic and Social Committee, which on this occasion was devoted to the eradication of poverty. "Poverty is spreading ceaselessly", said Annan, who estimated that an annual budget of $40 billion would be necessary to bring basic services such as education, health care and food to the poorest sectors, that half of the world's population that subsists on less than $3 a day. "Alleviating this situation", according to Annan, "is an ambitious objective, but not utopian". The only thing necessary to achieve it is the goodwill of the developed countries. Yet since 1992, these same countries

have reduced their humanitarian aid programmes by 24%, despite the economic boom they have enjoyed.

This is, in brief, the face of underdevelopment. But it is not enough to simply describe that face and evoke emotions, to make people "feel good" by turning generous for one day. It is necessary to analyse the causes of this dreadful situation, to understand why a large part of humanity —strangely enough, of "coloured" humanity, that is to say, non-white— suffers this level of degradation on a daily basis. I am all too well aware that by pointing out certain things so clearly I am running the risk of stirring up a defensive reaction in some people, of provoking the accusation that we black people who dare to speak or write clearly are "racist" or "revolutionaries". Yet my only aim in doing so is to stimulate the process of reflection that might lead to a solution to the problems, to a situation where all human beings can live in safety and with dignity. We do not want charity but justice, for we have been the object of international charity for more than a hundred years now, the object of the compassion of good and candid souls. Yet far from resolving our problems, the situation has continued to worsen. For this reason, many Africans believe that it is time to get to the root of the problem, rather than make do with palliatives. For these not only fail to solve the underlying structural problems, they also humiliate us, perpetuating in the minds of the rest of humanity the idea that we blacks are incapable of organising ourselves, of standing on our own feet, the idea that we must constantly be protected as if we were children who never grow up and must be guided and shown the way. Since no intelligent person can any longer doubt that we are human beings with the same attributes as the rest of the species, it would surely be logical to accept that we are perfectly capable of ruling our own destinies, no matter how much evidence there might be to the contrary. Our only aspiration is that the rest of humanity respect us, that justice finally extend its influence into all those spheres that touch our lives. For this reason it should be repeated once more, without resorting to demagogy of any kind, that the prosperity of Europe and the western world is based on the suffering and the misery of the African peoples. To say this does not necessarily mean we are "communists" or "revolutionaries"; in a final analysis we are simply a group of bourgeois who aspire to enjoying the same standards of living as we see elsewhere.

This aspiration is surely legitimate yet in the context of Africa it provokes strident reactions, since international political and economic relations continue to be dominated by selfishness.
To illustrate what I am trying to say, it should be remembered that there is not one single African country which is poor. Even those countries that appear most impoverished as a result of desertification, or other more or less natural phenomena (for the advance of the desert, with all the attendant ecological consequences, was brought about, or at least accentuated, by the abusive and untrammelled exploitation of the colonial period), even these countries possess other natural resources, such as minerals. Rationally administered, and with the proceeds of their sale invested in the development of the country, these resources would be sufficient to ensure the population had access to those basic services that dignify life. And here we have the two issues that, to my way of thinking, impede the development of the African countries: neo-colonialism and dictatorships. These factors are intimately related, and are the alpha and omega of all those other phenomena that derive from them and which are convulsing our continent.
Some fourty years ago now, the granting of independence to a series of countries was seen as the culmination of the struggle of the African people to recover their freedom after centuries of European domination, firstly through the slave trade, and later under colonial oppression. This struggle had coincided in history with the Allied victory in the Second World War. The side that fought under the flag of liberty, and of the inalienable right of every human being to enjoy a series of fundamental freedoms, defeated the forces of totalitarianism, which had reduced the status of the human being to that of a slave to the ideas of a few madmen. However, these struggles also coincided with other historical realities. Firstly, there was the reconstruction of Europe, based not only on the "Marshall Plan" but also on the exploitation of the raw materials and the very cheap labour of the African colonies. There was also the growing realisation of the cost, judged to be excessively high, of maintaining these colonies, which for humanitarian and economic reasons, had to be developed at least minimally, especially in terms of health services, education and infrastructure. And finally, there was the fact that the winning side included not only the western democracies but also the

Soviet Union, anxious to export its revolution to the rest of the planet, and if possible to other galaxies, a conflict that gave rise to the "Cold War". Thus, the access of the African countries to formal sovereignty was conditioned by this triple reality. The European powers granted independence but always subjected the new states to the political and economic tutelage of their former colonial masters, thereby ensuring their supplies of raw materials and guaranteeing their own continuing development and economic welfare. Thus, supposedly independent countries were controlled through the installing of puppet governments. Our Presidents became, in effect, new neo-colonial governors, a role they have continued to play up to now. For any of them who sought to defend the interests of their people, propagated ideas that did not coincide exactly with the role that had been assigned to them, or tried to introduce more liberating policies, was either overthrown or assassinated. Examples abound in the last four decades of African history. As a result, a ***coup d'état*** mentality has flourished in African capitals, and a whole string of tyrants have been spawned, whose only interest has been to assure for themselves, and for their families, the fruits of illegitimately obtained power. As long as they remained loyal to those who had brought them to power, it mattered little what they did to their fellow citizens. Think of Mobutu, of Macías, Bokassa, Idi Amin, Sékou Touré, Omar Bongo, Eyadema, or even Houphouët-Boigny, amongst others, and you will better understand what I am saying.

In this way, corruption took root in Africa, becoming the norm inherent in the system of power along with cruelty, nepotism and tribalism. The most horrendous dictatorships have carried out thousands of political assassinations, and maintain prisons where conditions are unspeakably inhuman, where people are tortured and humiliated in the most unimaginable ways. Put simply, what has been created is the police state, the totalitarian state. Rather than developing their countries in order to achieve the aims of independence, that is, the freedom and well-being of Africans, our political and military leaders have devoted themselves to amassing personal wealth. They have pillaged state assets and stolen international aid, which in many cases is paid directly into their private bank accounts in tax havens such as Switzerland or in major European and American banks. All this under the attentive and enthusiastic gaze of the West which, as long as their interests were being served, chose to overlook the murders and the looting, dismissed with indifference as "the blacks' way of doing things".

It was enough to label any dissident as a "communist" or "agent of imperialism" (depending on the regime in power) to justify the most horrifying violations of human rights. And thus the local population was cowed into silence since it was the government that possessed the means of coercion, arms of all kinds, supplied by the West. The local media are nothing more than an appendage of the repressive system, while those in Europe and America are not as independent as they like to proclaim and all too often, serve the interests of the members of their Boards of Directors, who are, in turn connected with the companies and other interests that exploit our natural resources. The result of this was that the immense suffering of the African people, and the struggles of the Africans against their tyrannous leaders, were systematically covered up, or else presented to public opinion as "tribal wars".

All this until the fall of the Berlin Wall in 1989, and the end of the "Cold War". At this point the world turned its gaze on Africa and discovered the horror. And this is the period we still find ourselves in today, a period in which it seems that there is no solution for Africa, for the hesitancy of the international community in applying the formulae that could bring stability to the continent is disconcerting, and at times demoralising, for both Africans and all those who study developments in our continent.

At the beginning of the 90s, Africa once more began to dream, as western countries began to recognise the ills of the continent and came up with the right answer, one which coincided with the aspirations of the African peoples and with the direction in which history was moving. In some European capitals, as in the United States, the idea began to be accepted that Africa could not continue to be an exception to the ideal of extending democracy throughout the world, and that the principle of the inalienable freedom of all human beings should determine the actions of governments everywhere. Questions such as the systematic violation of human rights, transparency in the running of the economy and the management of natural resources, and the principle that the political representatives of the nation states should be elected, should also be matters for action in Africa. Even countries directly responsible for what had been happening in this continent during the preceding decades, and what was still happening, began to link their future co-operation to the implementation of political change in the direction of democracy. However, the African dictators reacted quickly, as did the international financial interests that back them, and now, at the end of the decade, and the century, these promises have proved to be worth less than the paper they were written on. Although some changes took place in some countries, the overall reality is that little has altered, except in one highly important aspect: African people have become aware that freedom is possible.

In order to demonstrate to the world that Africa is “different”, that there democracy is “impossible”, we have recently been presented with the spectacle of especially shocking and repugnant wars, and of barbarous forms of repression. Conveniently, these outrages have received extensive coverage in the media –the same media which do not report the demonstrations in favour of freedom which take place in some African countries, or other matters that might benefit the cause of the liberation of oppressed Africans. Wars like those in Liberia, Sierra Leone, Congo-Brazzaville or in the Democratic Republic of the Congo are presented to international public opinion as “ribal wars”. Yet, in reality, they are nothing other than wars between the competing interests of those who speculate with our natural resources, wars for the economic and political control of our continent. In Liberia and Sierra Leone the struggle was over diamonds; in the former Zaire, the United States and France were contesting control of the immense wealth of the country; in Congo-Brazzaville, the oil company, Elf-Aquitaine, destroyed the hard-won democracy to reinstate a man who would guarantee their interests; in Angola the struggle was for control of the immense oil and gas reserves in the hands of the Luanda government and of the mineral deposits controlled by the rebel guerrilla leader, Jonas Savimbi; in Equatorial Guinea, Gabon or Togo, the American and French companies that exploit the oil and other mineral reserves have propped up the regimes of the eternal dictators against the manifest wishes of their respective peoples. And thus we could go on, from conflict to conflict, from country to country. And we may reach the conclusion that in Africa –with the exception of South Africa– there is not a single arms factory, yet almost anyone can start a bloody war with the complete certainty that they will find no difficulty in arming themselves

with the most up-to-date and lethal means of destruction.
And who pays for all this? In whose interests is it? In the answer to such simple questions as these lies the key to understanding what is happening to us. With this we can begin to understand why a large number of African intellectuals and professionals have been forced to flee into exile, for not only can we not work or live in our countries, we are actually seen as a problem. Here lies the key to understanding the reasons for the continuous and dramatic flood of refugees and of those emigrating for financial reasons, all of them fleeing from wars, from oppression, or from the lack of means of subsistence in their own countries.
This is the other face of underdevelopment. And it is important to underline that it is in this context that the international community is now clamouring against the injustice of the West's treatment of Africa, with a sense of outrage spurred by a series of issues that particularly incense the consciences of people of goodwill. These include the refugee camps scattered across the sandy wastes or hidden in the jungle, the return of slavery in Sudan, the anti-personnel mines, the reduction in the volume of international aid, the use of children as under-age soldiers and killers, or the burden of external debt, estimated at $222,600 million, the repayment of which currently accounts for some 70% of the economy of the sub-Saharan countries. In fact, in black Africa as a whole, debt repayments are running at four times the total spent on education and, in some cases, up to six times that spent on health care.
But these shocking figures should not make us lose sight of the fundamental objective of our demands, which must be the freedom, the liberation of Africa. As Africans, nobody feels more keenly than us what is taking place in our continent, in each and every one of our countries, home to our fathers, our mothers, our brothers and sisters and our friends.
Earlier we said that what we are seeking is not charity but justice, and this is the first goal we must achieve. And we need to ask for the help and solidarity of the peoples of Europe to do this, not to dig a well that we could very well dig ourselves. It is not a question of saving an African child but, rather, of saving all African children, together with their fathers and their mothers, their brothers and sisters, and of ensuring the necessary conditions of life so that never, never again will they, or their children, have to face an existence without a future.

Even though many Europeans reproach us for the fact that we always hark back to colonialism and neo-colonialism to explain the ills of Africa, this reality cannot be shrugged off, for the conflicts that currently exist in Africa can only be explained in these terms. The years since independence, which as we have already explained have brought neither the freedom nor the liberation of Africa, have been marked by the shock and disorientation that the impact of colonialism bequeathed to our continent, and which have still not been overcome. And this is even more true since Europe (and here you can read the western world as a whole) has not ceased to dictate to us what we should do, and how we should do it. Were there just one voice, the situation might be more bearable for we would know by whose injunctions we should abide. But from the developed world diverse, and sometimes contradictory, ideological or religious conceptions, fashions or recipes reach our ears, and the overall effect on the Africans is one of bewilderment. Every white person who crosses the Straits of Gibraltar becomes an "expert", and considers it beholden on them to explain to us what we should do according to their personal view, or according to the interests they represent. And all these recipes, including those of the new techniques and technologies —which in turn have given birth to new customs and new ethical considerations— are typically dismissed by the Africans as being "the whites' way of doing things", at times neither understood nor considered to be of any interest to the people. Some say, perhaps rightly, that it is not easy, or at least that there is a cost involved, in making the leap from the stone age to the atomic age, that Africa would have done better to have passed through all the intermediate stages between agraphia and the internet. Perhaps it is true, and Africa would have benefited from a more gradual process of its own, less hurried, and above all, less imposed, for in this way we would have entered modernity with fewer psychological traumas. But although we cannot turn back the clock, and things are as they are, perhaps at least we can demand for Africa, apart from behaviours which are more in tune with the ethical values of our times, a tempo which is less fraught. For certain phenomena need time to be digested calmly, and to be accepted with conviction. Make no mistake: there are certain minimum conditions that need to be satisfied if we are to, if not eradicate, then at least reduce the bitterness of conflicts, so that the social and political contradictions may be less enflamed and the life of each society may tend towards harmony. And these minima are enshrined in the Universal Declaration of Human Rights which every nation state, and every organised social grouping, should respect. Taking this as our starting point, every people should be free to choose their own model of coexistence, in line with their customs and conceptions of life, without being subject to excessive interference. For in the end, neither morality, nor ethics, nor aesthetics are rigid systems; there is no single model. Every nation, every age even, develops its own systems and so long as those of others are respected, without recourse to fundamentalisms, then the cause of peace is served.

Another of the questions which it is necessary to reflect upon concerns the social inequality, tribalism and systems of patronage fomented by the prevailing neo-colonialism, politically reinforced by the one-party rule that continues to function in Africa, despite the theoretical spread of multi-party political systems. This forces the entire population, especially the cultural elite and the civil service, to mould themselves to conform to the dictates of the powers that be. In this way they contribute to the transformation of the government into an omnipotent and omniscient State, from whose control nobody is free. Power such as this can only sustain itself by means of arms, coercion and fear, since it is exercised contrary to the wishes of the majority. Thus nobody should be surprised by the insensitivity of our leaders to the dreadful misery of the population as a whole, nor by their permanent resort to repression, nor by the systematic violations of human rights which occur in our countries. For those who govern do so only in their own personal interest. There is no alternation of power, despite the periodical calling of "elections" in which all kinds of underhand tricks are used, even direct pressure on the population, in order to ensure the victory of the governing party. Thus African military forces are, in general, private armies made up of relatives and members of the tyrant's tribe. In addition, the rulers, in order to stave off the threat of sedition, surround themselves with foreign militias, normally staffed by Moroccans, though in some cases by French or Israeli soldiers.

For all these reasons, the establishment of regimes that will defend freedom and the rule of law is necessary in Africa. But in order for the democratic ideal to triumph and consolidate itself, various conditions are necessary. The first of these is that certain European governments cease to interfere in Africa, and accept that recognition of the coming of age of the African people, and of their ability to direct their own affairs, means withdrawal of the support the dictators currently enjoy. Secondly, it is necessary to concentrate all our efforts on the education of our populations, as an essential means of emerging from underdevelopment, but also to act as a bulwark against permanent arbitrariness. It is also through education that the African people will acquire a national consciousness, which will be one of the ways of overcoming tribalism, and which must go hand in hand with the development of the necessary civic consciousness to create a scrupulous respect for every individual and their basic rights.

African development must also necessarily involve the acceptance by both Europeans and Africans that it is essential to extrapolate the concept of justice to commercial transactions and economic exchange. This would generate employment and welfare in the African countries and at the same time address the structural ills of the prevailing system, such as corruption. Much is said about this without taking into account that the person who seeks to corrupt is just as corrupt as those who allow themselves to be corrupted. Were this to happen, it would have a further positive effect. We Africans would learn to live from the fruits of our own labours and not, as happens at present, wait for everything to come from elsewhere, be it in the form of donations and aid, or loans whose repayment is avoided by a thousand and one subterfuges, or in the form of easy money through corruption.

The conclusion is obvious: charity is not enough to alleviate the misery of Africa and its consequences. Neither the dozens of bilateral and multilateral aid agreements, made with governments or international institutions, nor the solidarity of NGOs, have had any real effect at all. The African drama is the result of structural problems and these need to be addressed as such from all angles, on all fronts, particularly the economic and the political. That is, while the political world of the developed countries fails to realise this, assuming instead that they can continue to trade with Africa without the enormous majority of Africans suffering as a result, there can be no solution to this problem, one of the most fundamental and urgent of those facing humanity as we stand on the brink of the new millennium.

Emergency

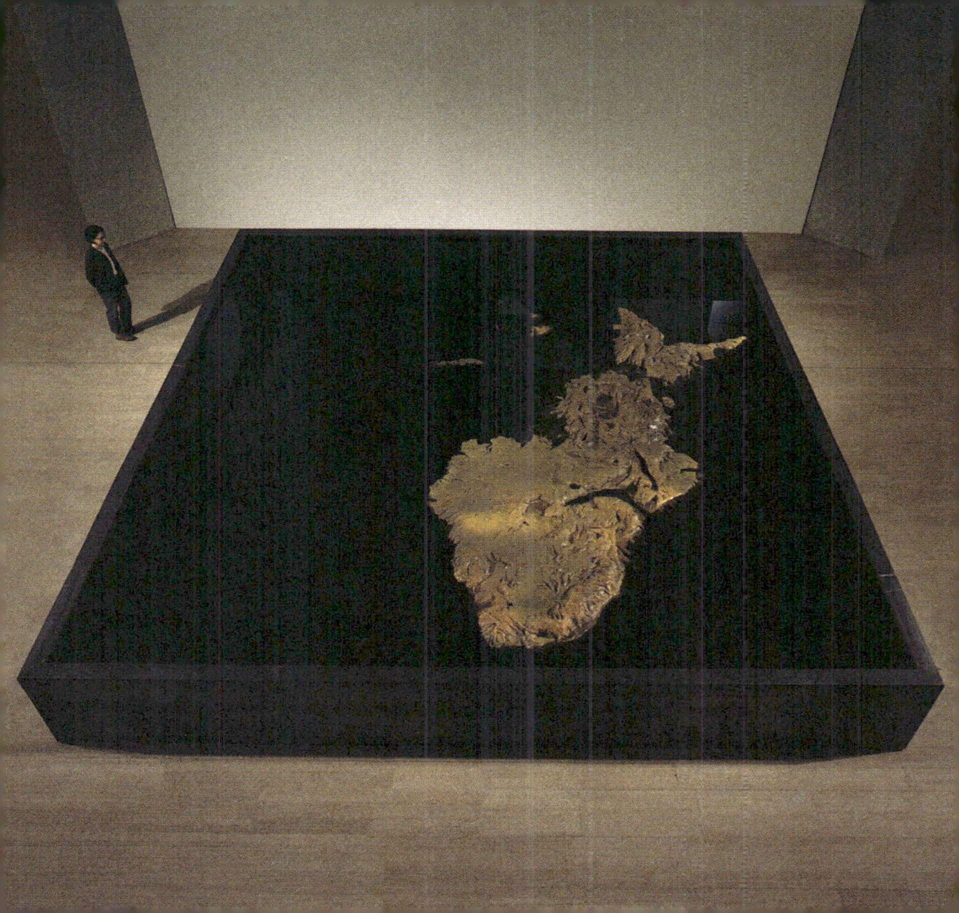

Alfredo Jaar
Emergency, 1998
Installation consisting of a metallic pool with water and a fibreglass model
750 x 700 x 90 cm

Africa: between tradition and modernity

If the general trend in Africa today is to leave behind tradition, it is no less true that the postures of reflection of those who seek to question the relationship between modernity and tradition are complex, whether they do so from an aesthetic, an ethical or a political perspective (this latter taken in its broadest sense, that of the way in which life is lived in the city). Only the integration of a renovated conception of tradition (understood as wisdom, and openness to otherness) allows the consummating of the brilliant marriage between myth and the mundane.

Tender, nostalgic or painful engagement between myth and the everyday world, an existence modulated alternately by its moments of emptiness and of plenitude, in thrall to the imaginary, and no less surprising than bitter reality, that which is transmitted never fails to return us to the world of the Ancestors, those distant hosts who haunt the past and who tirelessly launch us into the time that is yet to come.

For there may well be a cruelty in that transmission, yet no less cruel than that of the world itself, which either abstracts man from his abode, or else removes this world from him, stealing it from him in terms of the present. Thus, even the happiest of moments become tainted immediately, rendered precarious by that irresistible nostalgia for an ideal past which picks up on, and modulates, the dissatisfaction with the present. But the relationship with the passing down of wisdom allows man to install himself happily in the breach opened up by myth, a space that is never experienced as absurd or hopeless, but rather as offering a kind of plenitude yet to come, an embrace that is more insatiable and more vibrant than it is restricting, one which offers the purest form of enchantment.

If we think about it, there is no more radical revolt than that which tradition effortlessly exudes —at times so effective, and often so poignant, that trust is placed in the future as the only possibility, in change, or in the tremulousness of a present that is still being written. The ethos of the writer (his way of dwelling within and of seeing the world) leads him to work with myth in its intimate relationship with wisdom, in its sense that is at one and the same time ethical and aesthetic. The connection with tradition manifests itself as a way of staying close to reality, considered as elemental, primordial.

How, when faced with the simplicity and the marvellous fragility of this relationship, can we not reflect that, in reality, it is not always easy to say no to what one has been? In stories, in poems, it is to this rhythm, tenuous yet insistent, that black writing sets out to be faithful. In short, to a beat. And thus, to a tradition, even if it is evidently and incessantly necessary to rework it. To an oral form of expression, to a rhythm that is fleeting, subtle, imponderable at times, scarcely heard but always present, while at other moments its rhythm is clear and articulated... Rhythm, beat, sound, at the very heart of the freest flowing writing, the introduction of order, respect for a tradition that appears as a rhythm older than anything else bequeathed to us, that shapes us without our being aware of it, and that acts as a gauge of internal coherence, a coherence between yesterday, today and tomorrow.

An African myth explains that the life of a man can be divided into nine stages that together form a process of initiation. From birth to seven years of age, the infant, boy or girl, is schooled by the mother. The infant sees nothing other than her, understands nothing other than her, lives only through her. From seven to fourteen years of age, the child opens up to the world. To prolong the magic of the gift, from the moment of the earliest gesture, or even the first look, the child demands the radiant confirmation of the mother.

From fourteen to twenty-one years of age, the child begins to oppose his mother: an invisible knife is imperceptibly plunged into the most tender corner of their hearts, the wound bleeds and the future emerges drop by drop.

From twenty-one to twenty-eight years of age, he becomes a sieve where every hole leads to knowledge. The excitement is there, it gains ground, arouses, charms, pulls free...

From twenty-eight to thirty-five years of age, the deaf seed he carries within him moves, pulls away from absence, like a stirring, a motion, towards his future destiny. With a single movement, he consecrates and crowns all that he has lived so far.

From thirty-five to forty-two years of age, he is a man who has the right to speak in public. He is authorised to add his voice to the procession of those who question, but without providing any answers. For the next twenty-one years, that is, three times seven, he teaches, with the help of the elders.

From sixty-three years old onwards, the man is recognised as an elder, and professes without the help of any other. When someone consults him, he speaks with his hands on his knees, imitating the crescent moon. The fragile halo of the moon situates his teaching under the sign of fertility. Never will he use three words if two will do. Each and every one of his words is made up of twenty-eight knots that the person who consults him must untangle. He teaches every day when the moon waxes and wanes. Patient like the earth, which will devour us all after being trodden on by our indifferent feet, the elder always has the final word. His word will always shine, indecipherable. On his death, the elder returns to the eternal Orient, where he keeps watch over the glimmer of light that each day is revived, over the fiery plenitude of the word.
This myth shows that African wisdom is the learning of true measure. If there is rejection, dispute, it must remain within the interior of this measure, of this cadence, in internal exclusion. Taut, buttressed, always under tension, rhythm, the recognisable treasure of African voices, becomes the promise of the future, memory of that which is to come, an urge to invent even with the language, blending respect for and rejection of that which has been.
And the marvel is that this myth reminds us that African works compete to liberate, with their innate freshness, with their mysterious opacity, the voice that is the most authentic, the least tamed, the most innocent. For this is where the fusion between old and new and between myth and its message appears in its entirety, where modernity is tradition and tradition is modernity, where the slippery course of creation is in itself the objective, both ravishing and disturbing, that perpetual loss of an embrace and of a transfusion forever remembered.
Thus, marvellously free before a tradition that he never disputes, except internally, the African writer has, in equal parts, freedom and the precision that comes from being bound to that which is real, and sets about expressing the humblest, finest, most familiar parts of himself. He embraces his land, or rather, in the most natural way its imagery takes hold of him, he steps into this world and, at the same time, imperceptibly, introduces a secret element of metamorphosis.
Myth –in this very particular sense in which that which has been lived protrudes, hidden yet recognisable– has the acid freshness of the

everyday. There is a constant circulation from life to words and from words to life, a constant and sensitive shifting from real life to the imaginary and from the imaginary to real life. What writing sets out to uncover is the murmur of blood, the rippling of desire, the fragile birth of its own voice, of all that it contains that descries the future. The miracle of novel writing is that this movement duplicates itself: it is a movement descending into itself and, in addition, a laboratory, a crucible, an alchemist's furnace, in which the identity of a people and their destiny unfolds.

As myth introduces a confusing element into the narrative, to the extent that it blurs the ordinary contours of sense, it helps towards a chiaroscuro effect. The sharpness of seeing, that spark of wisdom, is inseparable from the disturbing impression of "seeing how", a metaphorical vision of the world that distils truths through the use of images, of symbols. The mythical narrative makes us receptive to the profoundness of that which can be sensed yet which, until now, has remained unknown, to an obscurity of meaning that enables us to inhabit poetically the flesh of the world. The wisp of straw that is man only gains substance in the shadow of the constantly renewed marriage of yesterday and today.

Like the myth that precedes them, the poem and the novel are not solely verbal objects presented for the mere aesthetic pleasure they confer. They are also projections of that which is to come, propositions for a world –a proposition in the sense of a possible way of inhabiting the African continent today and tomorrow. The true African writer should aim to make his work mark a horizon, the crest that signals the ardent promise of the future.

Reading African writers today means being aware not so much of the possibilities of a narcissistic contemplation of the work, but rather of the extent to which it offers itself as a reinvention of the earth, as a new configuration of the world, and proposes to its readers a new way of inhabiting the black continent. It is not possible to inhabit a space without meditating on the meaning of being-in-the-world, and the destiny of modern writing is precisely to be reflective. Writing also involves questioning oneself about the land and one's roots in it. But it also involves questioning the feminine as a condition for the possibility of meaning.

One of the hurdles that the African writer must overcome in order to discover this other being in himself, more stable and more truthful, is that of accepting woman in her totality as a being whose desire and curiosity are hinted at under her skin, in her gaze, in the words that reveal her to the world. Isolated in the current of a tradition that often makes them struggle against the flow, African writers must learn to discover the feminine gently, without taking control of it through violence and destruction, without destroying it. For femininity is what will enable them to reinvent their own land, to save it from oblivion or disaster.

Nostalgia for instinct, that violation of the being, which would once and for all deliver that which so many groping advances and retreats have scarcely been able to grasp, must be firmly rejected. Rather, the aim should be to accept woman in her most radical otherness. Another African myth, often forgotten, explains woman's reconciliation with the world.

When Zamba, the Lord Shaper of Souls, conceived human beings, he made them man and woman. From his mouth and his eternal word, he created the world and, with his breath, he bestowed on man and woman seven paths to knowledge: two ears, two eyes, two nostrils but just one mouth. Throughout the land Zamba, the Lord Shaper of Souls, was feared. All the inhabitants were afraid of him, for his word had been enough to create the world.

God spoke thus to the man and the woman: 'From your mouth shall emerge a double-edged tongue that will be capable of cursing or blessing; make wise use of this."

All the earth stood to the glory of Zamba; the exuberance of his creation was the work of his eternal breath. Zamba entrusted a servant to the woman and the man to watch over them. Having arrived in this world of perfection, the man gave rein to his anger; he hurled out knowing words and the countryside became smothered in darkness, the frail slivers of streams dried up, destructive lethargy took possession of the world.

His imprecations scorched the world's beauty as if it were stubble, perfection wilted under his curses, the light was eclipsed. The hand of Zamba called to the woman and the man. The servant, accomplice to the villainy, hid in the swamp, where he washed out his mouth and ears to forget all that he had seen and heard.

However, the curse of man rose from the earth, and the echoes of their crimes still resounded through all the confines of the earth. The sound reverberated in the ears of Zamba who exclaimed: "Their sin is grave! I shall call the woman and the man and demand of them what they have done". Before their Lord and Master, the man and the servant denied the damage they had done; the woman, in contrast, accepted responsibility for the misdeeds and accused herself of reopening the incurable wound of the world, of unleashing time, of injuring beauty:

"Please, let not the wrath of Zamba be stirred, I will confess".

However Zamba was not deceived and spoke thus: "Cursed be thee, servant! Since you have lied, you will remain deaf and mute for ever more. And you too, man, shall I curse! To you, who have lied and have incited the untruthfulness of the servant, shall come death... To you, woman, who happily accepts responsibility for a crime you have not committed, I give two further paths to knowledge, two breasts, through which you shall initiate men into life and loosen their tongues to the glory of the eternal". After these words, Zamba withdrew.

In this myth, the Divinity is not solely power or nostalgia for power; it is a dark force that retires into the night, having left the feminine and masculine face to face. The double portrait of Zamba –the first after the creation, an act of trust; the second after the fall, the putting to the test– confronts man with his nocturnal roots, with the internal guest who dwells within him, confused within the numerous meanders of his being.

To reach fulfilment, woman and man must, in the first place, immerse themselves and lose themselves in pain. This is something that can only be done by penetrating to the heart of myth, as in the story of Genesis, where there is only the cry, the essential wound, the sense of being hunted, the expulsion, the incurable uprooting. This they must do in order to avoid losing themselves in horror and perdition, in the fratricidal combats and the tribal quarrels. It is necessary to turn back towards woman who for long has been the humblest and the most humiliated, towards the one who did not hesitate, not even for a moment, to blame herself.

This is a matter of the greatest urgency.

Another myth explains that on the birth of a baby, an angel or a spirit that takes on the aspect of the father places a veil over the tongue of the new born child. This veil represents that which is forbidden, the law upheld by the father. The mother's milk slowly tears the veil, opening up the child to himself and to the world.

The sensation of what is coming or is simply desired being already present, the child and the mother participate together in their fusion into a single being. An essential part of existence is offered in the milk that is transferred from mouth to mouth.

This myth designates the feminine as the agent of the renewal of the world through language. It is to a present, to a virgin contact, opaque, unimpeachable, to which the child accedes when his mother speaks, when she teaches him to speak, when she becomes word, when the words that emerge from the mouth of the mother merge and blend as they are spoken to her child, are transformed into promise, like a gentle kiss.

Could we not, then, go so far as to say that the African mother, in raising her child for so long, confers on him a better chance of reaching the very place where the gift is made?

That which is heard in this irrepressible division of the world is neither the silent expression of Being nor is it a simple succession of everyday words. Rather it is a singular voice, that of the man of tomorrow, who, in a world that is alienated by violence and self-inflicted blindness, is capable of restoring true communication just like that child, a mirror for a whole continent, mutilated by the tyrants, a victim of a trivialising of violence.

In *Le cri que tu pousses ne réveillera personne* (The cry you utter will rouse no-one), my latest novel, published by Gallimard, one of the heroes, Doumé, the successor to Makaya, Chief of the Tribe of Honest Men, has been mutilated by some men who, before blinding him, had promised to take him to the city, to give him schooling. This novel is intended as an autopsy for a whole continent. Remember that St Augustine was obsessed by the suffering of children and that both St Thomas and Kant spoke of this as absolute evil. In blaming innocence itself, is Africa not compromising her future? This is the question which writers must answer.

Today, myth is without foundation. Nevertheless, the farewell to tradition does not mean grieving its total loss, but simply the displacing of its centre of gravity: stripped of symbols from the mythological past, myth has its use once more in the modern African novel, where, assuming a new function, it helps to nourish the hope of a poetic place to dwell within the black land.

Moving on myth

Africa? A book one thumbs
Listlessly, till slumber comes.
Countee Cullen

Africa as a book is an appropriate image, the continent is crammed with stories and multiple meanings. Africa's tales, their impact and their relevancy to modern African awareness are what I set out to discuss here. Unarguably, Africans share similar characteristics that stretch beyond the physical. Proximity brings about contagion if shared ancestry doesn't complete the job; we share the same consciousness, and yet we don't seem to realise it, properly realise it in a way that helps. By "consciousness" I mean value systems, dreams so bright its as if they sprang out of the hot earth and sang down from the sun at the same time as the first humans were loved into existence[1] at the rooster, iron and palm kernel place that would become Ife, the beginning of the world. It hardly needs to be said that we dream of life, success, and the peace and prosperity of those who share our bloodlines. Each African is a future protecting ancestor. And stories are my only way into this world, because I can look and look at modern Africa for hours, years, my whole life, saw open my head and cram it with rolls of printed-off statistics, death rates, birth rates, gross National Products of various years, and still not know where it is that I come from, what its problems are and have been, and how they will be resolved.

These aren't the words of somebody who is familiar with the colourful emergencies of Africa, the necessities of trudging to the well and back, swaying under the weight of clean, bucketed water in the absence of the tap variety, the 'growing accustomed to the dark' mentioned by Emily Dickinson, who, though she was talking about a different kind of dark, surely never had to heave an almighty sigh as the electricity cut off. Again. Rather, this is the muddled, tangential thought of someone who is "in" a Nigerian cultural framework but not "of" it, being carried along by a culture at a distance from its source and its pervading influence.

Let's define a mythology as a story system, a belief system. In an archetypal sense, the stories contained in the mythology are just as true as the world we see around us today. And a story that fits snugly into a mythology is ideally a series of images and symbols that have the power to reveal how people really relate to the world they live in. Anansi Spider, for example, embodies opposing forces of strength and weakness, the things that Africans admired in an agricultural based society where sourcing food was hard work. But he also reveals the traits that West Africans abhorred. The transformative power of the stories, however, was such that these flaws were turned into amusements that could channel the hostility away at the same time as acting as warning. Anansi is intermediary of the sky god Nyame, intelligent and patient in weaving his plots, yet he can be spectacularly lazy when it comes to honest work, is greedy and over-curious. He is inevitably defeated by his encounter with the wax girl, who, by being silent, maddens him to such curiosity that he attempts to touch her and is stuck to her. I immediately thought of Anansi's frequent skirmishes with Brer Tiger (who can forget his teaching the little monkeys to sing "I ate tiger's balls?") when I read that the anthropologist Claude Levi-Strauss argues that our mythologies about animals and nature reveals our tendency towards duality, the mental imagery of a clean break between opposites-good and bad, weak and strong.

So it follows that we build up a system of stories to ally ourselves to what we perceive as good and strong in our world. And the fruit that has fallen a little further from the tree needs to find other ways to place itself, a pressing need for second generation Africans is that of sorting out how they feel about the place.

As a mix of first and second generation –that is, born "back home", feeling more comfortable in my skin "back home", but embarrassed and often baffled by the Nigerian tendency to over-God things, to over-expect things, to be over-frank, I find Africa in the weirdest places, with the startlement of someone waking up in the middle of the night and catching a glimpse of themselves in the mirror across the room.

I have sat in mortification as a couple of Jamaican girls decided to call me "jungle bunny" in primary school, all three of us knowing that there was something temptingly wrong, actually hateful, in the name, none of us knowing exactly why. I've sat slit-eyed and exchanged glances of mixed embarrassment and defensiveness with another African whilst other classmates earnestly express their wishes to "help feed the Africans". I've nearly reeled with longing at the smell of camphor on folded traditional attire, wishing that I was back at my cousin's house, sitting on the verandah watching the heat chase lizards across the mosquito netting. My Africa are so personal that I can inevitably only replace "Africa" in my thoughts with my country Nigeria, of its various leadership crises, and of it's new hope under a non-military president who seems determined to battle the structure of corruption and bribery.

Yet this narrowing of the field of patriotic concern is indicative of a mindset found amongst most of the second generation Africans that I know, specificity is all. If I meet someone whose parents Nigerian, too, I'll eagerly enquire what parts they're from, and be philosophical if they turn out to be an Ibo (even though: "Never trust an Ibo!" a Yoruba friend of mine often says, half-jokingly. "They won't even think twice about killing you whilst you sleep...") and ecstatic if they are Yoruba. Even an Ibo, however, is better than, say, a Ghanian, with whom there is little to no point of contact. Word on the street is, we Nigerians stole *jollof* rice from Ghana. But do Ghanians eat *moin-moin* and *eko*? Have they had to put up with the flabby, sandy taste of ***eba*** until they got to an age where they could safely proclaim that actually they'd prefer a risotto? At times it feels dangerously as if there isn't a sufficient common culture, exotic annoyances that act on us in the same way as awkward, public kisses on the backs of our hands –influences to complain about yet at the same time be grateful for.

Its true that Ghanian kids must also have foods and customs that have helped to shape second-generationers' dual consciousnesses as Western types who sing into their mobile phones and slurp spaghetti bolognaise and yet can prostrate themselves before elders and eat *eba* (if they must) with an effortless pushing of some mental button. It's true that younger Anglo-Ghanians must also imitate their parent's accents as they exaggerate the parental complaints against "the way you kids do things". We all feel somehow that we will never be purely African enough for our parents at the same time as accepting that it's not our fault. But some divider exists between us, because our search for fellow Africans in our situation is selective: we're running around looking to see ourselves.

We need our stories back. We don't just need to share *Things Fall Apart, Yoruba Girl Dancing, The Gods Are Not to Blame*, and swap it for some of what Binyavinga Wainana and other African storytellers are writing. What we also need is to adjust the claim that the Arthurian cycle and Grimm and Perrault, et al, have on our minds and be told about how each of the first humans were formed to perfection in the stomach of Khepri, the Egyptian scarab beetle god, then ejected on a burst of air as sudden as if a Caesarian had been performed on a balloon. And Khepri wept with joy to see these first humans, and his tears brought the still shells of us, them, to life. Africans, Stories like that raise children and claim their allegiances by seizing their imaginations.

It is possible that Africa has reached a point where it can chiefly be thought of as a collection of countries rather than as a continent; we are each pre-occupied with our own locale because each nation is impossibly rich in its potentialities, its tendency towards existence on a Shakespearean scale, as if a fatal flaw charges through the continent like a roaring, dividing black stream, sharpening the edges of each country into a special affliction. Each country seems compartmentalised in its own challenges: South Africa's box is still layered with the thin fissures left over from apartheid, the shadow of preternaturally fierce children-made-soldiers starkly overlays the image of Sierra Leone, and Somalia and Ethiopia's names are ever twinned with starvation and poverty. As Nega Mezlekia notes in his outstanding memoir *Notes from the Hyena's Belly*, Ethopia is a place where a caste of unfortunates called the *Lalibelas* had to plead for freedom from leprosy every sunset so that they were spared the misery of having their arms and legs drop off, until they discovered that nothing untoward happened to them if they neglected to beg. Yet Ethiopia is also a nation that suffered under a communist junta and bore the widespread slaughter of youths when Haile Selassie lost power.

And Nigeria. In Nigeria, people who witches' belongings can be transformed into pumpkins: "And when they cut the pumpkin open, it was bleeding!" Respect for "traditional" beliefs runs alongside exuberant

Christianity, where Shango sprang, already crackling with supernatural power, from Yemaja's body with his brethren, or he was a powerful King who attained godhood when he hung himself, depending on how far you trace Shango mythology back, and in what area. The country may be a rich tapestry of beliefs, but the '80s and 90s saw the bleakness of rule by military junta: first Babangida, then his successor, Abacha, led the country in a state of fear and internal violence that had consequences branching from the execution of the environmentalist and writer Ken Saro-wiwa and eight fellow protestors for speaking out against the pollution of Ogoni (Niger-Delta) land by petrol companies such as Shell, to the death in Abacha's custody of Moshood Abiola, the President-Elect who was to have helped turn Nigeria around under an ideology of representative democracy. And Wole Soyinka, one of Nigeria's most phenomenal talents, escaped the turmoil of those times with his life –Soyinka was fast assuming the role of a Cassandra of Troy, cursed not to be disbelieved but to be suppressed in his country, unable to keep from warning of future peril.

In her novel, *The Secret History,* Donna Tartt observes that one of the most heartbreaking things about the development of a sense of "self" and "other" is the realisation that you are alone inside your head, that you are a sealed unit, and no-one can fully understand what happens inside you. For a while, it felt like this when I was being pumped with information about what seemed like the imminent collapse of my country. One of my friends was a Kenyan and another was from Zaire, and I couldn't talk about what was going on because the doubt and anxiety seemed so painfully unique; my parents were sick with fear over what their country was becoming, but their child was like a baby with her hands over her eyes, hoping that if she can't see you, then you can't see her. I didn't want to see what was happening to a counry that I had forgotten how to belong to.

Nigeria had been wounded, and it was bleeding people: Nigerians were leaving for Europe, and not just for ambitious educational purposes like my parents did. They were leaving behind weak life chances and coming to England, to a place where, according to a recent poll, 60%

of the population would "prefer not" to live next door to a member of an ethnic minority. To leave their homes for this veiled hostility suggested a huge problem: the Kafkaesque unease of it, the following of a niggling problem out of the corner of one's eye is excellently captured by writers who specialise in cataloguing Nigeria's blood flow, it's spillage into other countries. Writers such as Emecheta in *Second Class Citizen* and *The Bride Price* ask what's happening, and whether it's better away from Nigeria. The things I wanted to know about Nigeria when I was eleven or so were not: "We are living under a terrible military junta who are doing dodgy deals with what oil we have, and people are dying". I wanted to hear that:

> You must never write someone's name in red ink (unless they are already dead) because it means that they will die, and then it will be your fault.

> You must not whistle inside the house because it will invite spirits.

> If you drop your Bible on the floor, you will get a headache.

I needed to know what to believe in so that everything would be alright. And that was the problem with everything that was happening; with the attempted silencing of key creative minds like Soyinka (and who knows how many others?) Nigeria seemed, in one fell swoop, to have become a place in which it was impossible to dream. And if your country is inhospitable to your dreams, then so is the world.

So, though it seems a strange thing to say when the problems faced are so concrete and physical, but progress can only occur when ideas are reclaimed. Not the fevered, almost blinded embracing of Athenian democratic values by the French Revolution crew, or in reloading British and American values with "an African spin", but in balancing the old stories on our palms again. India and China, two other countries excluded from the "Western" pantheon, have their ancient literature, tales and heroes. In *Hind Swaraj*, Gandhi appealed to his countrymen for an India unified under its independence from Western Civilisation. He wanted Indian politics to be uniquely Indian, a modification of what had gone before. In doing this, he dared to propose that a nation could organise itself along the lines of its dreams.

It isn't difficult to see that playing at being European on land that has markedly different ideological undercurrents seems irresponsible somehow, like lions pretending to be whales and upsetting natural order. And though the ancient texts of the revered Koranic University at Timbuktu during the Mandingo-Askia dynasty are lost, we are rich in a literary culture too. We don't have a Genji, or a Rama and a Sita, but Eshu, the Yoruba trickster god who watches the crossroads of life (Esu in the rest of West Africa) acts as a hero on our landscape.

The story that comes easiest to mind about him is his best-known tale: Eshu was walking down the road one day, wearing a hat that was red on one side and blue on the other. No-one recognised him, and he passed through a village with his hat set on his head at a jaunty angle. The villagers asked each other what he thought was so funny, but they couldn't find out. And soon after he departed, the villagers who had been on the right side of the road and seen the blue half on Eshu's hat commented on "that laughing stranger in the blue hat". Some people who had been on the other side of the road, where they could only see the red side of Eshu's hat, started laughing. "Are you mad?" they said. "The hat was red." They eventually came to blows over the argument, each side feeling its intelligence had been insulted, until Eshu came back and cleared the mystery, teaching the villagers how fragile reality is, that it can be affected by imperfect perception. Eshu exists to expose us and make us think again, not unlike Loki of Norse mythology. But this is our particular humour, and this is our particular cunning, and stories like this, with or without Eshu as hero, abound across Africa.

The ideas channelled in stories must not be underestimated. For the stories a country tells about itself can act as a veneer, a special blanket of glamour that protects a nation, the quivering sackful of dreaming individuals, from the cutting gaze of others. African folktales in particular say, "this is who we were", in the most exuberant, vibrant way, unveiling the minds of a people so aptly that reading them makes a person shy, as if gazing at a beautiful, naked black woman who locks eyes with you,

knowing that you want to know more, or if you have previously encountered her, that you already know the satiny veneer of her skin. The words in myths wrap their arms around us and make us an extension of the godlike people that live in the raw, elemental world of our tales. The world was simpler then. And because of this, the tales survive: the characters take on lives of their own, become the orishas of Santeria and Voudon, remain loved while the country they came from faces a fall in its pride.
According to Durkheim, examining a society's beliefs is laying bare its beating heart. But Africa is having difficulties in presenting its scattered children with an idea of what it is. It's tales aren't matching up to its realities, and normally that's fine, but this continent cannot hide itself beneath its stories, its problems are well documented, and it shivers in the cold gaze of the media. When I think of newspapers, television, radio, websites, the whole information forum bundled into a concept, I can't help but imagine a wired metal eye that encages the meaning of struggle and suffering and makes it lesser.
Where printed words and the stattaco narrative of tele-journalism desensitise even the most attentive to the emergencies of Africa, a story works for me, one told by Nega Mezlekia, about a King in Shewa, Ethopia, who thought that he had heard all the original stories in the world, and offered a principality to whoever could make him cry out for an end to storytelling. Princes and landowners came to tell stories, but the King listened to their tales in silence. Then a farmer came along, causing the King to smile at his presumptuousness, at the very idea that he could succeed where other, famous storytellers had failed, and win land and a title. The farmer sat down and began talking about a peasant, saying:

"This peasant sowed wheat, then mowed it, threshed it and stored it in a granary when it had ripened. It was the best harvest he'd ever had. But there was a hole in the granary, a tiny hole, just big enough for an ant to get in through. And while the peasant was sleeping in his bed, an ant got in and carried away a piece of grain to eat".

The King was interested in the story, as it was not one that he'd heard before, and he urged the farmer to continue.

"The following night, another ant came along, and seized another piece of grain, and took it back for supper".

"Alright! Carry on!" The King pressed.

"The day after that, another ant came along and took another grain...".

"Hm!"

"And the next day, yet another ant came and took a piece of grain...".

"Yes, I see what you're saying," the King interrupted the farmer. "But what happened after all that?"

The farmer insisted that the grain-by-grain break down of the peasant's harvest was integral to the meaning of the story and continued describing the painstakingly slow plunder of the granary until the frustrated King cried out for an end to storytelling and was forced to give the farmer land and a title.
My argument seems to be that the future lies in reclaiming stories. How is this practical? How can a real, progressive effect be found behind strings of words? Well, Africa needs to become the subject of a self-fulfilling prophecy. It needs to be shown a reflection that it can aspire to. There is little chance that Africa's children can learn to love and believe in their country's capacity for freedom if they aren't spoken to in a language that they can understand. Like the farmer, imperturbably charting the movement of each piece of grain, we need to rebuild our history and our myth until the afflictions that exist, both present and lingering past, have no choice but to let us go.

1 For vanity's sake, let's say that the Yoruba were the first on earth..

Jean-Marie Vianney Rurangwa

Africa, who are you?

They say that poets are the prophets of the people. Prophets in the Judaic sense of the word, that is to say *nabí* (a man who speaks) as Marek Halter states in his book *Le Judaïsme raconté à mes filleuls* and not r*ohé*, which means seer. In other words, poets are the spokesmen of their people. They express their sorrows, their anxieties and their dreams. For this reason, Marek Halter continues, they are considered "political and social leaders, dissidents or revolutionaries". Poets have always taken on this political and social function, often at their own risk.
As a poet I am not pretending to change Africa through my words. My voice is too weak to perform miracles. Nevertheless, I am able to do something: bear witness. Yes! Bear witness to the suffering, the struggle and the hopes of this land that saw my birth, of this land that I love, of this land both rich and poor, of this land of tears and laughter, of this land shivering with cold beneath the summer sun, of this land which we know is dying, yet can arise from its ashes like the legendary Phoenix!
A son of Africa, born in this small country in Central Africa, this small country that my ancestors called "Ruanda Rugari Rwa Gasabo" and that we now simply call "Rwanda", this pretty country that tourists poetically call "The Country of the Thousand Hills", I have wandered I have wandered around the world in search of a place in the sun. And, as the singer Enrico Macias says, I have carried my country, Rwanda, and my continent, Africa, right there in the soles of my shoes!
And on my travels in the West, I have often been afraid, often been ashamed to say who I was and where I was from. I wanted to appear to be what I was not. And, deep down, I felt wretched. Until I remembered my mission as a poet, as a prophet, as a *nabí*. I remembered that I was Rwanda, that I was Africa. I remembered that I had to reveal my identity to the world with neither shame nor fear, that I had to speak for my people because I was their ambassador, that I had to explain their misfortune, their struggle, their suffering and their hopes.
So, to the curious who on several occasions have asked me who I am, I have replied without hesitation, "I am Africa". And they have insisted that I explain myself. Then I have asked them, "Do you want to know who I am? Do you really want to know what Africa is? Well then, I will tell you".
But what can I say?

Do I know myself well enough? No! There is a part of me that I do not know. A part of me that I am told about and that is prodigious. And who was it that once told me this? Ah yes! David Diop, my Senegalese brother! In his book *Coups de pilon* (Hammer Blows), he said:

Africa, my Africa!
Africa of the fierce warriors
In their ancestral robes
Africa of my grandmother's song
On the banks of her distant river
I never knew you.
But my eyes are full of your blood
Your beautiful black blood across the widespread fields
The blood of your sweat
The sweat of your labour
The labour of slavery
The slavery of your children...

Thank you, David Diop! To those who praise the Julius Caesars, the Alexanders, the Charlemagnes, the Napoleons, I too can praise the Chakas, the Soundjata Keitas, the Mansa Kankou Moussas, the Kigeli Rwabugiris, and so on.

But Africa is not just the Africa of warriors; there is also the Africa of the arts, of the sciences and of culture. Did not the specialists in African civilisations teach us that Ancient Egypt passed on its knowledge to Ancient Greece, which in turn passed it on to the West; and that the University of Timbuktu in Mali exchanged professors with European universities during the Middle Ages? However, we are unaware of this facet of Africa, or perhaps we pretend to be unaware because it is disturbing. Disturbing because it destroys something. Destroys the myths that served as pretexts for slavery and colonisation. The myths of the "barbaric, savage, stupid, half-man half-animal" African. Voltaire gives some idea of these myths in his *Lettre d'Amabed*:

"There is a serious problem with regard to them [the Africans], that of knowing whether they are descended from apes or whether apes are descended from them. Our sages have stated that man is made in the image and likeness of God: behold, then, a droll image of the eternal Being with a squashed black nose and little or no intelligence! Undoubtedly there will come a day when these animals will learn how to cultivate the land, make it beautiful with houses and gardens, and when they will find out about the movements of the heavenly bodies. There is a time for everything." (Voltaire: *Lettre d'Amabed*, t. XXI, cit. in Ki-Zerbo 1980: 316)

This text of Voltaire's justifies the inhuman conditions in which slaves were forced to live for four centuries! Indeed, what could be scandalous about chaining up an animal and branding it with a hot iron? However, these "animals devoid of intelligence" had been able to create prosperous empires all over the black continent. But of course, the sugar cane, cotton and tobacco plantations in America were in need of labour, and only "animals" could work there in the conditions that we are all aware of. The slave trade that tore more than one hundred million people away from the black continent was replaced towards the end of the 19th century by something equally lamentable: colonisation.
Here too a pretext was needed: "to civilise the savages and convert them to the Christian faith".
So it was that in 1885, in Berlin, the great powers of the time shared out the African cake behind its owners' backs. And overnight the African peoples were transformed into British, Belgian, French, Spanish, and Portuguese subjects! Everything still needed to be done in this virgin continent where the savages "had neither invented nor created nor sculpted anything...".
Thus, the theory of the "clean slate" is used to justify the illegal occupation of African lands by Europeans. However, the real motive was that European industries needed raw materials and Africa was full to the brim with them! The Frenchman, Jules Ferry, never tried to hide the real motive behind the colonial design. "Colonisation —he stated— is the child of industrial policy." But to soothe the conscience of the settler, the missionaries brought with them a theory of equality between Christianity and civilisation. With this in mind, Aimé Césaire, the Martinique poet, wrote in his short book *Discours sur la colonialisme* (A Discourse on Colonialism) that what contributed most to the racism of which black, indigenous and oriental people were the victims, was the hypocrisy of the missionaries who created two false equations: "Christianity=Civilisation, Paganism=Savagery".

In this way, a white and Christian (in other words, "civilised") minority imposed itself upon a black and pagan (in other words, "savage") majority, with the aim of allowing Europe to take maximum advantage of the abundant riches that Africa offered. And so, products such as sugar, coffee, tea, bananas, cocoa, minerals of every kind, oil, and wood were carried off to the West, while the majority of black people were plunged into abject poverty.

In order to assert their authority, the settlers kept native people in a state of inferiority by applying the principle of the colour bar. In every colonial town or city there was a European quarter and a native quarter, as described by the Cameroon writer, Mongo Beti, in *Ville Cruelle*.

The indigenous society was divided up into two, the "developed" and the "non-developed". A native who had gone to school, who spoke the language of the colonisers, and behaved like them, either consciously or unconsciously, was considered "developed". This "developed" person was the one who served the settler as an assistant for those tasks that were undertaken in the colonies. The colonial ideology that justified the presence of the European in Africa was based on the superiority of the white race and on the inferiority of the black race. Prejudices and stereotypes were exploited to the maximum: "Coloured people do not have the intellectual capacity and moral qualities needed to organise themselves and exploit their country's resources. They cannot govern themselves without lapsing into anarchy and despotism. Colonisation has civilised them, has taught them...".

The white man went on to become a demigod in the eyes of Africans. Many natives did what they could to assimilate, but in the colonial context, where assimilation did not imply equality. And so it was that, however well the colonial subject spoke the language of Voltaire or Shakespeare without any trace of an accent, he would never be on an equal footing with his European master.

Unable to live like his ancestors, whose culture he despised, and unable to be on the same level as the white man he was trying to imitate, the "developed" native's life was, quite simply, the tragedy of a poor uprooted individual.

However, this situation would not last for long. Black African intellectuals raised their voices to denounce the assimilation and enforced cultural change of Africans. They preached the idea of returning to one's roots to reclaim dignity and personality. And that is how the concept of negritude was born! Negritude! Negritude! Let's talk about it! It's worthwhile! Aimé Césaire, creator of the neologism, defines it as "the simple recognition of the fact of being black and the acceptance of this fact, of our destiny as blacks, of our history and of our culture".

For Senghor, "Negritude is the specific way in which the values of civilisation of the black world are absorbed, and when necessary, brought up to date and enriched through outside influences".

Negritude came as a real shock. It was a shock because it was a surprise: people who had profited from Western culture were speaking of the restoration of black African values! Could it be that black Africans had something that deserved esteem and respect? Yes! Anthropologists and ethnologists had revealed the cultural riches of the black continent to the West.

At the same time, negritude, or Black Awareness, seemed to some like a kind of racism. Indeed, we had never heard any mention of "White Awareness" or "Yellow Awareness"! If negritude is a form of racism, retorted Jean Paul Sartre, "it is an anti-racist racism". The black man has been humiliated, insulted, and despised on account of his race. He must therefore assert himself through his very race. "He gathers up the word 'black' that is thrown at him like a stone and stands proud...".

However, the recovery of the black African race and culture was not possible within the colonial context. The African could not be himself, could not be proud of his race and his culture while bent double beneath the lashes of the colonial whip. For him, the struggle for liberty turned into a *sine qua non* in his search for total fulfilment.

Aimé Césaire had nothing other than this in mind when he said:

"What does black youth want? To live. But to truly live, you have to be yourself. An actor is a man who does not truly live. He brings to life a great many people –playing many different parts– but he does not bring himself to life. Black youth does not want to play any part: it wants to be itself. The history of black people is a tragedy in three acts. First, blacks were enslaved (...). Then they were looked upon indulgently (...) and an attempt was made to educate them. They were assimilated (...). Now, blacks want neither slavery nor assimilation. They want emancipation."

The struggle for the liberation of Africa was not an easy task; it was hard and bloody. Africans ran up against the resistance of colonial authority, which wanted to maintain the ***status quo***. But liberty is one of the most fundamental rights of man and, sooner or later, he will end up achieving it, whatever the cost. Thus, around the 1960s, the wind of independence blew across the black continent and brought great hope to the people who had long lived there in slavery. The people of Africa would finally be masters of their own destiny. Out of this emerged some very luring ideas: Panafricanism, African Unity, the Africa of the Africans, etc.
Independence arrived and the people enthusiastically composed odes in honour of the "Fathers of the young nations". How beautiful liberty was! But the moment of disillusion was not long in coming. These same people, whose new leaders had promised any number of miracles, saw their hopes dashed when the young republics were transformed overnight into fascist dictatorships. The heads of state became cruel, irresponsible, treacherous, tribalistic and nepotistic tyrants. From an economic point of view, the continent made no progress. The colonial authorities had not created the necessary infrastructures for the exploitation of all the resources that the African continent had to offer. They had given no training to an indigenous workforce that might have allowed the continent to board the train of progress without having to resort to foreign aid.
The divisive ideology that the settlers had planted in the minds of the indigenous people to better assert their authority bore fruit the day after independence. From North to South, from East to West, Africa fell prey to fratricidal wars for the benefit of the dictators and their Western allies.
The disillusioned people asked themselves whether or not they had been given independence. A Congolese writer described the situation very well: "Colonisation has only changed colour. Now it is black". And from the moment of independence to the present day the people released from colonisation have sought in vain to warm themselves in the sun of liberty and prosperity.
If anyone would like to know what the century that we have just left behind represents for Africans, I would tell them without fear of contradiction that it has been a disaster. Hardly had Africa escaped from colonial oppression than it found itself at the mercy of the most odious tyrants! It was left without children, who were condemned to

exile because of terrible and bloody wars! It was left without intellectuals who, through fear of being incarcerated or eliminated for their ideas, took refuge in countries where freedom of expression was more or less guaranteed! If "Black Africa has started badly', to quote René Dumont, I would say that it has also ***ended up badly***. And the end of the century did finish badly, with bloody wars in the south in Angola, in the east in Somalia, in the north in Algeria, in the west in Sierra Leone, in Burundi, in Rwanda and in the centre, in the two Congos. And, at the end of the century, the catastrophe culminated in the genocide of the Tutsis in Rwanda. A genocide committed by a member state of the UN and the OAU against a section of its own people, right under the nose of the International Community! A disgrace for the Africans who looked on with indifference as Tutsis died like animals in the slaughterhouse! A disgrace for some Western countries that supplied material aid and media support to a regime that brought about the genocide in Rwanda! A disgrace for the International Organisations that guarantee respect for human rights! A disgrace for all those who, after the genocide of the Jews under the Third Reich, had said: "Never again!".

The "Interahamwe" militiamen stripped this slogan of all its meaning. After the genocide of the Tutsis, we have to ask ourselves if people will go on saying "Never again!" And yet, it has to be said, the tragedy which plunged Rwanda into mourning in 1994 has demonstrated perfectly that it can happen all over again anywhere in the world if the members of the Great Human Family do not pay more heed or do not consider the disasters of other people, however far away, to be their own!

The genocide of the Tutsis in Rwanda! A Rwandan drama! An African drama! A human drama! Allow me to write here what I replied to the curious who, shocked by the genocide of the Tutsis in Rwanda in 1994, kept asking me: "How did you come to this?" The genocide of the Tutsis has nothing to do with the other genocides that have been perpetrated up until now. The acts of genocide against the Redskins were committed by the European conquerors; the genocide of the Armenians was perpetrated by the Turks; and the genocide of the Jews by the German and Austrian Nazis. The genocide of the Rwandan Tutsis was perpetrated by Rwandan Hutus. One part of the Rwandan people wished to exterminate the other part of the Rwandan people.

Another peculiarity: in the course of the genocide of the Tutsis in Rwanda there were many cases in which the executioner and the victim belonged to the same family. So, for example, a Hutu man killed his Tutsi wife and the children that resembled her. A Hutu woman killed her Tutsi husband and the children she had had by him. Many Tutsi mothers were murdered by their Hutu sons. Incredible but true!

Now I go back to the question I was asked: “How did we come to this?” Did the famous Hobbesian formula *Homo homini lupus est* apply to Rwanda in 1994?

To understand the tragedy of Rwanda in 1994, we must first take a look at the history of this country. According to Anthony Giddens “The past is the mirror into which the sociologist must look in order to understand the present”.

The history of Rwanda shows us that the genocide of the Tutsis in 1994 is neither a random event nor “a reaction of the people maddened by the assassination of their beloved president Juvénal Habyarimana”, as claimed by the deniers and revisionists of the genocide of the Tutsis, but rather the fruit of a racist ideology instilled into the Hutu population by the exclusively Hutu regimes that came into power between 1959 and 1994. But the bases of this ideology date back to the times of the explorers and the missionaries. And this is how!

Books by Arthur Joseph de Gobineau, Wilhelm Marr and Houston Steward Chamberlain appeared in Europe in the second half of the 19th century. These authors put forward racist theories according to which there were superior races and inferior races. They stated that the Aryan race, as represented by the Germans, was the superior race. The Aryan race should dominate the other races and lead the world towards progress. When Adolf Hitler wrote *Mein Kampf*, the bible of anti-semitism, he was greatly inspired by these racist theories. And as everyone knows, the fruit of his labours was the Shoah!

The first visitors to Rwanda read the anthropological reality of this country through the looking-glass of the superior races and the inferior races. Indeed, when the Europeans arrived in Rwanda towards the end of the 19th century, they were surprised by the existence of a monarchy which was as well structured as Western monarchies.

A Tutsi king reigned over a people consisting of three social groups

(Hutu, Twa, and Tutsi) that spoke the same language, Kinyarwanda, were united by a single culture, and lived side by side in the same land. Each group had its particular activity. The Tutsis mainly took care of cattle-raising, the Hutus agriculture, and the Twas hunting and pottery. This does not mean that the Tutsis could not cultivate the land and the Hutus could not raise cattle.

These three social groups, even with the same language and the same culture, exhibited quite noticeable somatic differences. However, this should not have seemed strange. There is not a single country in the world in which all the inhabitants have the same somatic features. But we are talking of a time when people believed in superior races and inferior races!

According to the European visitors, the Rwandan monarchy was so well organised that it could only be the work of a superior race. Undoubtedly originating from somewhere else. And surely not black! The "black savages" were incapable of organising themselves, according to the prejudices of the time! And so it was that an explanation was found for the Rwandan mystery: the Rwandan people are made up of three different races (the Twas from the pygmy race, the Hutus from the Bantu race, and the Tutsis from the Nilotic race according to some, the Semitic race according to others and even White according to yet others). That is the Hamitic theory!

The Austrian explorer Oscar Baumann, the first European to visit Rwanda, thus wrote in his book *Durch Massailand zur Nilquelle* that the Tutsis stood out on account of their slender build and their almost European look, which had given rise to the legend of the "white negroes".

Similarly, the missionary Louis de Lacger did not think twice about writing in his book *Le Rwanda Ancien* that "the Tutsis who came from Egypt or Abyssinia were brothers of the Nubians, of the Galla and of the Danakil, who were of a Caucasian type and had something of the Semitic from Ancient Asia about them, but had black skin".

Jean-Paul Harroy, a long-standing resident of Ruanda-Urundi, in his book *Rwanda. De la Féodalité à la Démocratie* maintained that the Tutsi, apart from the colour of his skin, had nothing of the negro about him. Monseñor Léon-Paul Classe wrote in 1902 that "the Tutsis were proud people with fine, regular features, and of a somewhat Aryan and, also, Semitic type".

His companion Ménard stated without reservation that "the Tutsi was a European in a black skin".
From their arrival in Rwanda (at the end of the 19th century) until 1959, the Europeans favoured the nobility of the monarchical regime of the Tutsi majority (this being part of the policy of indirect rule, or indirect administration) to the detriment of the Hutus and the low-ranking Tutsis. At first, schools were only for the children of Tutsi chiefs and lesser chiefs who, after completing their studies, were to work as assistants to the colonial authority in all its spheres of activity. These "beloved children" of the colonial authority were judged by their "racial superiority" to be the only ones capable of getting the masses to work within the twofold colonial design: the administration of the territory and the evangelisation of the people. Monseñor Clase stated that for this the Tutsi element "was the best, the most active, the most convinced, the most suitable to play the part of the social yeast or catalyst".
But everything changed when in 1959 the leaders of the UNAR (Rwanda National Union), the monarchical and nationalist party of the Tutsi majority, demanded Rwanda's immediate independence. The leading protagonists of the Rwandan colonial scene, that is to say, the Belgian settlers and the Catholic Church, were annoyed by the demands of the UNAR. In fact, they had no intention of giving up their power to the natives. From that moment on, the alliances were reversed.
The Belgian colonial authorities and the Catholic Church headed by Monseñor Perraudin, abandoned the Tutsis of the UNAR, now deemed to be "communists" and "anti-European", and gave their total support to the Hutus of the MDR-Parmehutu (Democratic Republican Movement, also known as the Party of the Movement for the Emancipation of the Hutu). Most of the leaders of this "ethnic" party had been educated in seminaries, and therefore enjoyed the confidence of the Catholic Church and, most importantly, they did not speak of immediate independence. The Tutsis, who up until that time had been the "beloved children" of the colonial authority, now found themselves being insulted for having dared to demand that the Belgians leave!
These "white negroes" who came from Caucasia, Egypt, or Abyssinia were called "foreign invaders, colonisers and secular oppressors of the people of the Hutu majority".

Liberty and democracy for the Hutus of the Parmehutu, who from then on were supported by the Belgians and the Catholic Church, were synonymous with the departure or simply death of the Tutsis. It was not the Belgians who were to leave Rwanda and return home to Belgium. It was the Tutsis who were to leave the country to its "legitimate owners" and "return home to Caucasia, Egypt, Ethiopia or Mesopotamia!". Incredible!

President Grégoire Kayibanda, spiritual son of Monseñor Perraudin, President of the MDR-Parmehutu and President of the Republic of Rwanda from 1959 to 1973, declared in September 1959 that "the Parmehutu sought the well-being of the Hutu group which had been offended, humiliated and despised by the Tutsi invader". He stated that "(his) duty was to teach the Hutus and restore the country to its rightful owners. Rwanda is the country of the Hutus".

Grégoire Kayibanda did not take long to apply his ideas. So, beginning with what he called the "Social revolution of 1959", millions of Tutsis were cruelly murdered, irrespective of age, sex or status. Thousands more went into exile in neighbouring countries. The Tutsis who survived these acts of genocide and who remained in the country were treated as second-class citizens; but what am I saying? They were treated as aliens in their own country! Kept away from every important sector of the life of the nation, these Tutsis served as scapegoats every time the country went through a crisis.

During the thirteen years that Kayibanda's rule lasted, expressions such as *Inzoka* (snake) and *Inyenzi* (cockroach) were used to refer to Tutsis. The "revolutionary" songs extolling the "democratic republican" Hutu and demonising the "feudal monarchical" Tutsi were frequently broadcast on Radio Rwanda. And Tutsiphobia captured the collective imagination of the Hutu!

When in 1973 Major General Juvénal Habyarimana, Grégoire Kayibanda's Defence Minister, overthrew the latter in a *coup d'etat*, the Tutsis believed for a moment that they would finally be able to breathe. But how disillusioned they were when Major General Juvénal Habyarima established the policy of "ethnic and regional balance of power", a pure and simple euphemism for Rwanda-style apartheid. This policy, which officially sanctioned the discrimination against the Tutsis, this time

affected, albeit to a lesser extent, the Hutus who did not come from the President's native region.
Nonetheless, Westerners continued to help and support this "saintly dictatorship", to quote the expression used by Colette Braeckman. When the Rwandan refugees subject to persecution in the countries in which they had taken asylum asked to be allowed to return to their country, Habyarimana, without any scruples, answered: "The country is small. There is no room for you. Stay where you are".
This categorical rejection led the Rwandan exiles to form a politico-military movement, the RPF (Rwandan Patriotic Front), which recruited its members not only from the Tutsi diaspora but also from the interior of Rwanda amongst those who felt oppressed by the regime. Among the principal objectives of the Front figured the return of the Rwandan refugees to their country of birth after thirty years of exile. The Front launched a military attack on Rwanda on October 1st, 1990.
Unmasked by national and international opinion, Habyarimana and his acolytes launched an anti-Tutsi campaign to cover up the evils that were devastating the country. The ideologists of Hutu extremism, in the pay of those in power, competed in insulting the Tutsis, and their incendiary speeches brought to mind those of Reinhard Heydrich, Joseph Goebbels or Adolph Eichmann against the Jews under the Third Reich.
The ten commandments of the Hutus, published in 1990 by the extremist newspaper *Kangura* ("Awake!" To be understood as "awake the Hutus, against the Tutsis") recalled the racist laws of Nuremberg. Like the Nazis who wanted a Europe that was *judenfrei* (Jew-free), or rather *judenrein* (purged of Jews), the "Rwandan Nazis" wanted a Rwanda that was *tutsifrei* (Tutsi-free), or rather *tutsirein* (purged of Tutsis).
When on 6 April 1994, on his return from Dar-es-Salaam, President Juvénal Habyarimana's plane was shot down over Kigali, the Hutu extremists seized on this attack as an unexpected pretext to perpetrate a genocide that had long been planned. The Tutsis were brutally murdered without regard for age, sex or status. Those Hutus who had not adopted the ideology of genocide were also murdered. And so Rwanda experienced the Apocalypse! Not what the Jewish prophets had foretold, but rather what had been predicted by Théoneste Bagosora, the man who General Roméo Dallaire, then commander-in-chief of the forces of

the UNAMIR (the United Nations Assistance Mission for Rwanda) called the Devil. As this Canadian officer was heard to say, “I believe in God because I have seen the Devil: his name is Théoneste Bagosora”.
As he was hastily leaving Arusha (Tanzania), where peace negotiations were going on between the RPF, the NRMD (National Revolutionary Movement for Development) of Habyarimana, and the opposition parties, Colonel Théoneste Bagosora had announced: “I go to prepare the Apocalypse”. The following day, April 6th, he kept his promise!
The Rwandan Patriotic Front put a stop to the genocide in July 1994, with its victory over the Army of the NRMD. It formed a government of national unity with the parties of the opposition. It inherited a country that was physically destroyed and a people that was ravaged and traumatised, consisting of orphans, widows, the mutilated and the displaced. While withdrawing into Zaire, the genocidal army and government had forced into exile two million Hutu civilians who, in the refugee camps of Zaire, faced cholera and the threats of the Interahamwe militiamen who held them hostage.
The anti-Tutsi campaign continued in Zaire, where Tutsis were murdered by the local populace with the assistance of the former Rwandan Armed Forces and the Interahamwe militiamen. Then the so-called “Banyamulenge” war began, forcing the Hutu refugees to return, overthrowing Mobutu and bringing Kabila to power. However, it would seem that Kabila did not honour the agreements that he had reached with those who had helped to bring him to power. Once again another war, against Kabila this time, which involved the intervention of at least five countries in the region: Uganda, Rwanda, Zimbabwe, Angola and Namibia. And so now you have the entire African Great Lakes region at war! The peace negotiations achieved nothing in the way of concrete results. The belligerent parties continued to leave their populations in the most appalling chaos! Meanwhile, the countries in the region, in the same way as certain Western powers, chose their allies according to their own interests from amongst the brothers at war with each other. But, in all frankness, if in Africa it is the Africans who make war, they do so to a large extent with the logistical help of the West. But everyone wants there to be peace in Africa! But everyone weeps and prays for these poor blacks who kill each other, instead of uniting to combat hunger, sickness

and ignorance! But everyone knows that from the time of independence till the present day, tyrannical, totalitarian and bloodthirsty regimes, instead of working for the well-being of their peoples, incite tribalism, corruption and extortion, arousing feelings of frustration and resentment among the people affected, which inevitably leads to fratricidal wars.
But everyone knows that these regimes still go on benefiting from the support of the Western powers because they guarantee the interests of these powers in Africa!
So let's stop shedding crocodile tears! If we preach hatred and sow discord between brothers, we will have fratricidal wars and genocide! If we embezzle public funds, our countries will always be poor! If we do not cultivate our lands, we will die of hunger! If we do not build schools, we will live in ignorance! If we do not build hospitals, diseases will wipe us out! If we live by the sword to rule our peoples, our peoples will live by the sword to end our days!
And let's have the courage to shoulder our responsibilities! Let's not blame everyone else! Even though everyone else helps us to dig our own graves! A Rwandan proverb says: "Fire is given to the one who wishes to burn down his hut". Enough said!
I would like to finish by recognising before my readers that here in these lines I have not told them all that I am. Nevertheless, I believe that I have given an idea of what I was before having the chains of slavery clapped on me, of what my masters thought of me before fastening them round my neck and my feet, and what they said of me to make me wear them without causing them any kind of remorse.
In the same way, I think that I have given an idea of what I was when the whip of colonisation lashed my back in the name of Western civilisation and the Christian faith, and of what I did to reclaim my freedom and dignity. Finally, I think that I have given an idea of what I had hoped for and what I actually experienced during the time of "reclaimed freedom".
And if someone were to ask me to sum up in a few words what I have been during this century that we have just left behind, I would simply say that I have been:

An Africa that suffers, that weeps and that dies.
Yes! An Africa that bows and begs for alms!

A tribal Africa, a racist Africa!

A warlike Africa, a genocidal Africa!
That's right! And if they were to ask me to sum up in a few words what I would like to be in the century that is just beginning, in the third millennium and in the times thereafter, I would say that I would like to be an Africa that does not know what it means to have an empty stomach.

An Africa where those who chant in the Mosque *Allah Akbar, Mohamed Rassour-Allah* (Allah is great, Mohammed is his prophet) do not look in fury on those who make the sign of the cross in the Church and say: "In the name of the Father, the Son and the Holy Ghost. Amen", or on those who sacrifice a black cat in the night in the name of their ancestors' souls, so that they may receive protection for their children, their animals and their fields!
An Africa where those with straight noses are not the enemies of those with flat or hooked noses!
An Africa where those with fair skin do not want to exterminate those with dark skin.
An Africa that is curious to find out what is happening in other parts of the world but that does not dream of going to the moon while its children have nothing to put in their mouths!
An Africa that learns the lessons of the past!
An Africa that believes in solidarity, an Africa that is sensitive!
An Africa that dances to the rhythm of the tom-tom but that also knows how to dance rock and roll, reggae, samba and –why not– the waltz!
An Africa that is happy, free and dignified!
An Africa of which Africans can, at last, feel proud!
"What a lovely dream!" my readers will probably say. What difference does it make? I prefer to dream of a radiant Africa than to heed those who say that Africa is cursed, that Africa is doomed for ever by an implacable fate.

Nkosi sikelele Afrika!
(God bless Africa!)

Brussels, December 1999

José Eduardo Agualusa

A future for Africa

Pessimism is the privilege of happy peoples. In most African countries, people are either optimistic, or they die, there is no other option. And so they laugh, in the midst of the disaster, and with two beers they start a party, and they dance, they dance a lot, and the rich countries, seeing them like that, shake their heads in dismay and say: "The Africans are going mad...".
They don't understand how laughter can exist for people destined to die. Frightened, they look on at our fierce, urgent gaiety, unexpected like a bright spell in a storm, and they withdraw again into their dark houses.
I am also optimistic. I can see the Africa that is coming: I can imagine her splendid figure –resigned and mortified, yes, but above all, splendid– emerge from the dark waters of nightmare. I can see a new African man, his heart beating for his ancestral land –with all that that implies for his spirit and readiness for celebration– and, nevertheless, totally capable of using knowledge to explore the triumphs of the modern world.
I imagine the "Carers of Ancient Times", the women that the Angolan poet Mário António de Oliveira wrote about: "Carers of another time/ I can see you in that yellowing picture. / Black hair, long and loose. / Elegant clothes nobly worn / and the hieratic bearing of the bodies. / I see you during a festive afternoon. / Did a boat anchor in the river? / Was business going well with such a crowd? / Perhaps the miraculous saint was being celebrated, loaded with offerings in the chapel. / Carers of ancient times / the ladies of young men and disciples / promoters of business and trade (...) / Carers, you sense the intimate, obscure unity of mystery and purpose (...)". I imagine these "Carers of Ancient Times", rescued for another time, for this century which is now beginning, where profane science may be added to their knowledge from long ago.

Africa is important for the world

African people are important for the rest of humanity. Africa gave music to America: negro spirituals, blues, jazz, soul and rap. With the black hands that they stole from African lands, the Portuguese created Brazil.

Despite the innumerable disasters which affect our continent, African people continue to give the world examples of their gaiety, tolerance, creativity, their capacity for loving. Nelson Mandela, after being held in prison for a quarter of a century, came out to embrace his jailers, and with this great gesture saved South Africa, becoming, together with Martin Luther King (an Afro-American) and Mahatma Gandhi, one of the greatest heroes of the 20th century.
The African people who migrated to Europe, and their descendants, rejuvenated the Old World. The descendants of the African slaves in North America, the Caribbean, Central America and South America invented new colours, new rhythms, different tastes, different ways of telling the same story of humanity: Basquiat, Nicolás Guillén, Gabriel García Márquez, Jorge Amado, João Ubaldo Ribeiro, Machado de Assis, Patrick Chamoiseau, Richard Wright, James Baldwin, Langston Hughes —and so many, many others.
The great tragedies that push man to the limits of Life, in direct confrontation with his worst demons, have always been a source of inspiration for art and literature. A people that has solved all its problems is a people awaiting death. I believe that the enormous cultural vitality of our continent will be able to express itself totally this century, as new ways of communication such as Internet, in their essence democratic, establish themselves and find their place.

How we can change the way the wind blows

Africa's unhappiness started with slavery. Millions of Africans, especially young men, were captured and taken across the seas. Certainly it is not coincidence that the word meaning "sea" also means "death" in many African coastal languages, including the Kimbundu language in Angola. Huge territories became practically deserted. Deprived of their most valuable men, entire nations began to decline and never again were they able to recover their lost splendour. It was then that Africa began to die. European colonisation, organised around the black slave trade, deepened old social divisions, created new ones, broke up traditional social

structures, massacred, destroyed and devastated. When slavery, that huge exterminating machine, ceased to function and the African peoples were finally freed from colonial oppression, what was left was a continent whose population, dignity and memory had been stolen.
African people are expected to forget all of this. On the contrary, I consider that it is important to remember. Nevertheless, instead of crying over spilt milk, we must try to use in our favour some of the results of European politics in Africa. Healthy and tasty fruits do grow on rotting trees. For example, thriving Creole societies emerged in the New World because of slavery. These societies and the black community in the United States, with increasing political and economic power, must rediscover Africa. American people of African descent can put pressure on their governments to help reconstruct the continent. The same goes for the African communities established in Europe, who, it must be said, still have not lost their links with Africa.

Democracy as a condition for development

It is a fact that some of the problems that our continent is facing at present are direct consequences of the Berlin Conference, which took place at the end of last century. The colonial powers which organised this event established political borders according to their own interests, with no consideration at all for the indigenous populations. It is also a fact, nevertheless, that most states in the world have artificial frontiers (with the exception of some islands, many of them in Africa, they all do), and they are multiethnic and multilinguistic. Switzerland, for example, is an old and stable country which consists of several different nations, each one of them with their own language.
Diversity means richness. A healthy ecosystem is a space rich in species and which works towards diversity. On the contrary, a sick ecosystem works towards monotony. The same thing happens with human societies. Democracy is the only political system that I know of which is capable of peacefully administrating the conflicts that may arise from this diversity, and gather together projects and ideas. In Africa, as in the rest

of the world, there have always been democratic societies and others subjected to totalitarian regimes. If Western countries want to help in the reconstruction of our continent, which I understand to be in their interest, first of all they must support the democratic forces and destroy the tyrants.

Why we cannot doubt

Each time I read in the newspapers bad news about Africa, especially Angola, I remember the strange object I discovered when I went to visit a rehabilitation centre for the mutilated in Viana, a small town near Luanda. At first I thought it was a piece of modern art. It was a collage of twisted pieces of iron that vaguely, but very vaguely, resembled a human leg. A nurse saw my startled look: "It's a prosthesis", she said, "well, it used to be a prosthesis." She told me that a few months before an elderly farmer had come to the centre. He had walked from a small far-away village in the north and had used this strange apparatus as his right leg. He had lost his leg at the beginning of the sixties, almost four decades before, when he trod on a mine. He was aided by Portuguese soldiers and before going home was given an aluminium prosthesis. This broke several times and he patiently repaired it himself, with barbed wire, tape for shells, old iron, in fact anything he could get hold of. In the end, this wonderful burden weighed twenty five kilos. When they gave him a new prosthesis at the rehabilitation centre, the man (the nurse told me) beamed: "Now", he whispered, as if he was about to tell a secret, "I'll be able to dance again".

On another occasion I interviewed a gardener in a town called Huambo, where I was born. For years he had worked in the Cold Greenhouse. After independence and with the start of the civil war and the departure of the Portuguese technicians, he was left alone, as if he were the guardian of a secret garden that for most people held no interest at all. In 1994 Huambo was invaded by the guerrilla forces and the city was bombarded for fifty-five days by the government aviation. Many people died. People hid in holes that they had dug under their houses and they stayed there, day and night, drinking rain water to check their hunger, or "eating water" as someone said to me. Despite the situation, the gardener went out every morning, facing the din of the bombs, to go to the Cold Greenhouse. I wanted to know what pushed him to risk his life like that. He gave me a simple, knowing look: "The roses needed watering". Thanks to this gardener, to the mutilated man in Viana, to all the simple sons of Africa, I learnt not to doubt. On 20 July 1969, the poet Ernesto Lara Filho turned on a small radio to hear a report on the saga of Apollo XI. Next to him, a farmer was also listening to the moving words of the astronaut Neil Armstrong. He hugged the poet and said: "One day, brother, we will also have to plant cashew trees on the Moon".

It will be so, one day.

Marlene van Niekerk

Heat and history down South

“You have to get security”. My father looks at me sternly wiping sweat from his brow. “Priority number one, do you hear me? Flat steel bars. Cottage pane. Small enough. They push the children through to open up from the inside”. He demonstrates the square that would bar a five-year old and jabs his finger into the windowsill at regular intervals. “With pop rivets. Like this. Nothing less. Understand?”.

“Nothing less”, I nod. I size up the large windows of my new house. Through the huge trees on the pavement I can make out the profile of the Stellenbosch mountains trembling in the noonday heat. “It will cost,” I say my head blank with the deep shock that besets all people that move house.

“Just do it”, he says, “first thing”.

“It’s too hot for discussion”. I put more ice in my tea.

“Something else,” my mother says trying to change the topic. “You need a proper mattress on a proper base. That sponge thing you’re sleeping on is very bad for your back”.

I notice a furtive thought entering her gaze with a host of unwanted associations in its wake. She adjusts the angle of her head, careful not to offend. My mother has mellowed with age, has forgiven herself fo the double bed standing in her single daughter’s bedroom.

“A Sealy”, she says.

“On a Sleep-eas...” My father sips his cold tea

“A Sealy Posturepedic”, my mother insists. “Medium resistance, the one stitched with small diamonds”.

Again I put more ice in my tea. According to the weather bureau it was 43° in the Western Cape. The hottest December in fourty two years.

“How am I going to get one single line written in this heat?” I ask aloud, half unintentionally.

“You will get used to it”, my father says,

“One gets used to everything” my mother says, an ominous innuendo flexing itself underneath the slack skin of cliché. Has she forgiven herself for having forgiving herself? I wonder.

I am in the bosom of the family. Up country where I lived for more than 15 years and before that when I studied in The Netherlands, I was far from the heat in more than one sense. With its cold dry winters and cool wet summers, Gauteng’s capital, at 1.900 meters above sea-level, has one of the most pleasantly temperate climates in the country. I will miss it I realise even though I often felt terribly alienated in Johannesburg: a rough-shod den of money grabbers, gut toters, traffic jammers as it has always been since the discovery of gold in the previous centruy.
But this is another country, and 1.400 km to the south. The old people still ironically refer to it as “the Colony”, reacalling the days of Dutch and British rule. It has a Mediterranean climate. Long hot summers and mild winters with penetrating rain. The weather of my childhood –bean soup, hearth fires, story-books with pictures. But it is changing. The summers are getting drier and hotter each year: rainfall figures are dropping.

“The effects of global warming”, my father says. He also has his moments of flat resignation. A retired civil servant, who worked for the previous government in the department of Agricultural Technical Services, he watches the world with a beady eye, meets its challenges with the only means of defence that is left to him, a quirky peasant sense of humour.

“It is the Adversary”, he quips, “checking his thermometers for teh melt down”.

“It is Karmic”, I counter, admitting at the same time to be a chip off the old block, party to the same metaphysical bent when it comes to interpreting the ways of nature.

“Karma, is Buddhist, isn’t it? I prefer the Devil”, my father says.

Again the heat stifles all argument. It won't help to ascribe it to an external force, I could have said. It is simply a form of retribution, evil returning in a wayward form to tose who initiated it.

For years Stellenbsoch University had prided itself on being home to "the great leaders of the nation". Almost all prime ministers of the Apartheid period had studied here and had cut their political teeth in the arena of student politics. It used to be a kind of nursery for the teachers and policy makers of the so called Christian National Education, for the clergy of the Dutch Reformed Church (both instruments with which the white Afrikaner Nationalist government had grafted its racist and pseudo fascist doctrines onto the people).

I close my eyes, the central factor of the move hitting me squarely between the eyes for the first time. I never thought that I would come back here to my home town so to speak, where I went to high school and university, the place of my first youthful rebellions and transgressions, the terrain where I first engaged armed only with enthusiasm, with those problems of identity that, in a very specific configuration, beset this southern tip of the vast African colonial/post-colonial territory: problems of class and gender, "race", ethnicity, sexual identity.

I remember that not many years ago the Titanic-like building, in which I am now going to teach, was officially called the John Vorster Building after the prime minister with bulldog jaw to whom Breytenbach had deddicated his famous butcher poem: "does your heart also stiffen in your throat / when you touch the snuffed out limbs / with the same hands with which you will carress the secrets of your wife?"[1]. For years there were protests and the students started referring to it as "The John". Finally the name was scrapped from the statute books and renamed as the Arts and Letters Building. It might be a while still before it is called the Adam Small Building[2].

It is highly likely that here the so-called "African Renaissance", the heroic cultural motto of our new president, will be piously analysed by the true blue Stellenbosch academic arse-lickers. The same ones who analysed with the same deference, Vorster's policy of 'Detente' in the seventies.

Same tongues different arses. Or are they so different? Is the new danger not once again nationalism? Only this time a blunt essentialist African nationalism? The thought suddenly explodes. Like a mutant cell it multiplies into a mass of half formed ideas and sentiments.
In the seventies The Tongues probably did not know the verb from which 'detente' was derived. It is doubful whether Vorster could conjugate anything in French and it is equally unlikely that the new leadres would know how the noun "naissance" is derived, let alone any of its other derivations and applications.
Être née. Née Van Niekerk. Stayed Van Niekerk. I suddenly remember that my name was supposed to be Jacqueline and not Marlene. The banns for my christening were already read in church when fate struck. Sir Seretse Cama, the previous president of Botswana, then Bechuanaland, a British Protectorate, had scandalously married a white woman, Ruth Williams, in the fifties and their first child was born at the same juncture as I was. She was to be called Jacqueline. It was front page news. Enough at the time for my parents to change their mind about naming me. They told me later. The story had stuck in my mind. A pity in a way. People would have naturally called me Jacke after my father, who has areal Afrikaner name, Jacobus Everhardus, but who is generally known as Jack. It would have suited me better than the slightly effete Marlene that nobody knows how to pronounce. My first Dutch lover used to calle me Lili Marlene in bed with a naughty accent. I have a suitcase, still, in Amsterdam. I think. I must have it sent here now.

"You are quiet". My mother looks at me. She is unpacking a box of kitchenware together with my father, who handles my possessions with something like good humoured scepticism.

"Very quiet". he says, "moving makes one quiet. You have too many porcelain bowls, child".

"It is the heat", I say, "I'll go and have a shower".

I am grateful for the heat, the shower, the escape that it offers. It all suddenly feels too much. "Come now, old girl", I talk to myself in the mirror, "you have lots to be grateful for. You have a job. You have dear dear parents and tomorrow the cats come. There's a start to be made".

Towards the late afternoon my parents leave. My mother has stocked my freezer with dozens of recycled magarine containers full of cooked food.

"For the first few days", she says, "I know how it goes".

"Curried mince" I read on the lids. "Stewed peaches. Spiced venison".

"You must have your roof cleaned. With a power pump. Twenty bar. Nothing less. But first cut down that damn tree".

"Call us when you need us", he says gently as he gets into the car.

"Keep well in your new house". My mother blows a kiss through the window as my father reverses out of the driveway. I notice how white their hair is. The next few days pass in a blur of heat and unpacking. I get a sore elbow from cutting through the tape with which the packers had sealed the boxes. Hours after their arrival my Persian cats still sit panting like dogs. I keep them indoors for a few days to accustom them to their new surroundings. They look at me questioningly when evening falls. I can't leave my windows open at night because there are no burglar bars. I sleep with a hastily bought fan switched on full blast over my naked body. In the thick whirling luke-warm air, I lie, pondering trying to get grip on the situation. I think: I have a house in Africa and I'm struggling with a two-headed African angel: Heat and History. A climate that makes intellectual effort seem superfluous. A history that swings to a pendulum rhythm of colonial dispossession and post colonial reappropriation.
A week before New Year's day a bomb explosion rips through a restaurant in Cape Town. It is set off by a mobile phone mechanism at the exact moment when the police arrive. A police woman looses a leg through the force of the blast. It seems to be another in a series of explosions in Cape Town over the recent months. The device used is

brutally improvised. It is called a "pipebomb". Loose shards of metal and nails stuffed into an arm's lenght of plumbing pipe. The bombs all went off in venues of popular entertaiment and all caused heavy casualities. The police flounder and bungle. No-one claims responsibility. No-body is apprehended. Sinister political motives are suspected. Police involvement is rumoured. The Minister of Law and Order, previously of Sport, announces that a "safety net" will be extended over the entire Cape Peninsula in the holiday period. No-one believes that it will be effective. Too many empty promises have been made lately. The most commonly heard interpretation of all this is that the liberation of the country had brought in its wake typical phenomena of post-authoritarian societies: crime, corruption, lack of control and accountability in state departments and crude gestures of entitlement. The most obvious sources for the authenticity and the origins that people seem to crave are ethnic identities and religious fundamentalisms.
I am an African. I am a Muslim. I am an Afrikaner[3]. These are sentences that one often heras. The insistent tone of these phrases betrays the "nervous condition" to quote the Zimbabwean writer Tsitsi Dangarembga caused by the crisis of self understanding gripping the country. This is poignantly illustrated by the case of white Afrikaner intellectuals who have supported the struggle for freedom but have now started to voice openly their strong misgivings about the high-handed attitudes of the new goverment and its apparent lack of both will and skill to fulfill its promises to the people.
In my case all the symptoms of the crisis have been exacerbated by the move. Who am I? What am I doing here? I mend a leaking tap with an old pair of pliers. It belonged to my paternal grandfather. He was a miller and a poor white. My father was the only child that went to university. He went without shoes until he was sixteen.
At five o'clock in the afternoon I desperately start watering the arid soil around my house. And after that I even more desperately salt the sanils that come out to take the moisture. I sit up in the backyard for as long as posible, loathe as my cats are, to enter the stiflingly hot house. The moon

is full. Its presence every night seems as relentless as that of the sun in the day. According to the newspapers it is at its brightest in one hundred and thirty three years. When I finally go to bed, I am drunk with the apprenhension that its fierce mad light seems to stir up in me. I envisage my little life as a single brief pulse of light like that of a fire fly in the reeds with the only difference that it shows up only once.
I realise that the move in itself is probably an index of much wider historical trends. In a way I am just another statistic in the rising number of people, who can afford it and are leaving the north of the country out of a growing unease with the rampant crime there. And in another way, I am a mere statistic in the number of academics adjusting to the changes taking place at universities: diminished state subsides, falling student numbers, shifts in the enrolment patterns. Students choose commerce subjects and courses in information technology. Languages are definitely out. Bad news for the Renaissence.
I start out on the first of many forays into town: I identify the hardware shop and find out what a pop rivet looks like. I locate the nearest café, automatic bankteller, supermarket, the chemist and a furniture shop, where I sit down on a few intimidatingly sprung, stitched mattresses.
I visit an old friend from my student days, who survived a brutal attack by a rapist a few years back. She resisted, fought him off, landed in hospital with seven stabwounds and a collapsed lung.

"I live in a fucking cage now", she says pointing to the burglar bars on her verandah.

"But that's life, honey. That's life".

I struggle with the telephone people and the post office people. The former are sluggish beyond belief to get me connected, the later just shrug when I complain about the registered cheque that got lost in the post.
Service down south sucks as in the rest of the country and there is no significant difference between the para-statals and the private companies. At the Vodacom shop, where I finally submit to buying a mobile pone, they manage to sell me, from a sealed plastic container, a

second hand simcard throwing up on the phone's little screen, names and numbers of people that I don't know from a bar of soap. Bitterly irritated by the heat, the mosquitoes in my stagnant swimmingpool, the unremitting screeching of the cicadas that envolopes my new house, I go back to complain.

"No wonder", I say, "that people can set off bombs with these bloody things."

No great shakes, the assistant changes the card.
Driving back home I conclude that the only difference down here is that I can speak to most people in my mother tongue, Afrikaans. I find that, although it doesn't seem to have any special effect, it does make me feel more effective. I can joke with the black people. The familiar extends beyond language. I seem to recognise faces without names to put to them as yet. The dormant map of the town, that I carried within me all these years, slowly awakens. I recognise streets, remember how they fit together in spite of the town having coffe shopped and side walk terraced itself almost beyond recognition. Stellenbosch is in the Herat of the Cape winelands and has become a major tourist attraction. I often hear German and French. The tourists walk around in the heat with the gay abandon of holiday makers. They bear it with the masochistic ejoyment of sightseers. This is The Great Other. This is Africa with air-conditioning they can all afford at night. Stellenbosch offers them both curio shops with African trinkets, superb wines and *gourmet* foods together with mountain views reminiscent of southern Europe. There could be a Petrach lurking somewhere.
On one of my shopping excursions I stop dead still on the pavement at the sound of a certain type of exposition, last heard in my student days when I studied philosophy as one of only a few women in huge classes filled with serious, closely shaven, white male theology students. The professors at the time were also mainly theologians. I look around. In the unbearable heat an old main in khaki safari suit with long socks turned over at the knee is explaining in professorial terms to a younger

man the intricacies of the Holy Spirit. He talks about its outpouring and its being received. I glance at the monographs stacked on the little table, the sermons of Andrew Murray, one of the first Scottish Theologians that came to this country. I recognise in the conversation Greek words spoken with great deference: pneuma, pleroma, the wind, the fullness, the over-fullness. There is pathos in this. The old man is clearly a retired academic of the old school and of the old politics. Now that his sting has been pulled his learning has become a quaint relic. I apareciate it for its thoroughness. There is knowledge of Greek there. A language through which certain specific things can be interpreted, remembered, felt. All that is beginning to belong to the past now. Departments of Classics, and of Semitics were some of the first to go at the universities, followed closely by those of modern European languages and comparative literature.

Even before I can properly assimilate news in the chaos that surrounds me I start buying the newspapers, two or three at a time. It is a habit from the height of the struggle days when the urgency of events, the mile posts in the process of liberation were what we lived by. Now there is nothing uplifting and very little reason to hope for even a moderate measure of progress.

The holiday deathtoll is way beyond eight hundred. In Western countries this would be enough reason to call for the resignation of the Minister of Traffic and Transport. Dullar Omar, previously minister of Justice announces one after the other toothless "Arrive Alive" campaign.

Many historically disadvantaged schools will once again start the new school year withouth sationary or school books. The Minister of Education, Kadar Asmal, fromerly Minister of Water Affairs seems unable to stem the flow of the mismanagement and incompetence in his department. The University of the Western Cape, which is owed 40 million in unpaid student fees, announces that it is lowering its entry requirements because of the drop in student numbers.

Many people in high places seem to be in trouble. The new Comisioner of Police, Jackie Selebi, formerly South Africa's representative in Geneva, is

not recognised by a female sergeant in charge of a station that he spot checks without announcement. She behaves unco-operatively. He calls her a "fucking gorilla". She now lays a charge aginst him of crimen injuria. Helena Dolney, widow fo the late Joe Slovo, vacates her director's seat at the Land Bank under a cloud of alleged racism and self enrichment. She is quoted to have said that the pressure brought to bear on her is part of a movement of "ethnic cleansing" of progressive whites form the upper echelons of state management.
Just before Christmas, during a world conference of religion, Presiden Mbeki himself refuses to see the Dalai Lama in private. It is rumoured that his decision was influenced by diplomatic pressure from China, with whom South Africa has recently forged diplomatic and economic ties. Not much joy in reading the *Cape Times* on a hot day. I turn a page just to tumble from the disgrace of the local detail to the disaster of the global. According to a yearly United Nations report on the wellbeing of the planet, the challenges facing the South are nowhere so critical as in Africa. Poverty is quoted as the biggest cause of environmental decay and depletion of natural resources. On a continet racked by political instability, protracted wars and the world's worst HIV and Aids epidemic, environmental questions end up second on the list of governmental and aid organisations priorities. The report mentions the likelihood of a second co-operate colonisation of Africa: many African governments have already become intimately linked to one or more big international companies for the sake of survival.
Maybe I should become a consultant, I think, soaking in a cold bath. Then I can recommend to government the advantages of a "Cuban" rather than an "Italian" gesture. That is, instead of brandishing about an utterly inappropriate notion like the Renaissance, to decree that all state officials shall henceforth drive themselves around in Volkswagen City Golfs. The rhetorical effect of such a gesture might be needed before the next election. The natives, me thinks, are getting restless once more.
I have to attend my first social dinner in Stellenbosch. It is a relief to know that I will be accompanied to the rather upmarket and predominantly

heterosexual party by a close friend, a lover of yon and until recently a colleague in the Department of Afrikaans at the University of the Witwatersrand. She is on her way to Holland. Immigrating. "Returning to the Motherland", she calls it with due irony.
Getting out of colonial territory to start a new life on home ground. Her phrasings don't quite ring true. The rationalisation seems too easy. We are from South Africa, born here, easily the tenth generation. We both felt the weight of that fact as we took photographs of each other a few days prevously against the backdrop of the massive three hundred years old camphor trees at Vergelegen, the estate of the colonial Dutch governor Simon van der Stel in the 18th century. The rough grey bark framed us fatefully, we felt, encrusting us on the cusp of perilous transitions. We lingered for a long time in the sumptuous gardens. The estate belongs to the Oppenheimer dynasty these days and is considered one of the most important historical sites in the country.
At the dinner my friend and I both automatically withdraw to watch and to judge "the embarrassment of riches" to quote Simon Schama[4], with which we are so irrevocably complicitous. The converation is light and very entertaining. The food is good and studiously evokes the past: a feisty Malay curry. The wine is very old. Most of the people know each other, some of us were students together at Stellenbosch, some of our lecturers of those days are present, three of us attended the landmark ANC writers conference at the Victoria Falls in 1988, two years before Mandela was released. There we signed our support for the cultural boycott of South Africa until such day as freedom came. All of that seems very far in the past now and the idealism of that gesture rather naïve.
The current topic stands in sharp contrast. How to stuff a paw-paw with heavily spiced duck. The recipe, Malay once again, is conveyd with relish and a lot of clever literarely referenced sexual allusion.

"'Stellenbosch mischief'!" I whisper into my friend's ear. Our hostess picks up on it, smoothly extending the quote from the movie *White Mischief*.

"Another fucking beautiful evening in the Boland" she says.

With our shared smiles we acknowledge our finally honed skill of treating with irony our priviledged situation. We live in a country where fifty percent of the people survive on an income of less than R300 per month. Suddenly as though the trickster god, Hermes, himself had entered and kicked over the wine, another note is sounded. The voices, all male are raised. There is tension in the air. The subject is violence. The horrifically high incidence of rape and sexual abuse of children in the country. One in two women will fall victim to rape in her life time. An example is offered. It concerns the contentious sentence of seven years imprisonment recently passed by one Judge Foxcroft. In his verdict he gave as reasons for the relatively light sentence that the crime did not pose a serious threat to society (it happened in the bosom of the family) and secondly that the defendant, fourteen years old, claimed that she did not want to see her daddy rot in jail. One of the people at the table is a lawyer. Without batting an eye he turns to me:

“The sentence is more than adequate. Do you realise what will happen to that man every single day of the seven years that he will serve in any South African jail?” He gestures unambigously to indicate male rape.

It is enough to lure me from my perch. I attack viciously feeling all the time that I lack the poise, the fast arrows and facy footwork of my youth. My heart beats very fast. I feel how I turn blood red in the face. I have to concentrate on a very long sentence:

“How dare you, as a lawyer, imply that real justice is meted out on another level than that of the courts and how can you defend a judge, who lacks the moral courage to extend the context of jurisprudence to a general ethical point of view?”

I feel the hand of my friend on my shoulder.

“Come now”, she whispers in my ear. “It’s not worth it. He’s drunk and he’s a man”.

We drive home in silence. I unlock a boiling hct house and check the rooms while opnening the windows to let in fresh air. The cats are out in one leap. We drink iced tea.

“Maybe he was right”, I say.

Swirling the ice in my drink, I recall the thesis as I understand it of *Disgrace*, the Booker Prize winning novel by J.M. Coetzee. If we want to stay here in the country as women, as single white women we will have to absorb every posible violation. To relinquish all that we own and to be possessed and repossessed as female bodies by the masters of the land. That is the real pattern of justice underneath all the talk of human rights and reconciliation (and “Renaissance” come to think of it).

“Coetzee is not a lawyer and he is not drunk. Where are the black intellectual who must question his grim prognosis? They are to busy whipping up their African Renaissance to be bothered by white writing”.

I am overwrought.

“What will become of me in this place?” I cry while my friend fills seven ice trays with water.

The relief is only temporary. When the tears cry up I find a newspaper cutting that I thrust into her hands. She reads it shaking her head. It is about remarks made by a black female member of the parliamentary committee on the promotion of Equality and Prevention of Unfair Discrimination Bill. The committee had to hear recommendations of several interest groups among them the National Coalition for Gay and Lesbian Equality. “I say, society doesn’t understand what s all about. Define it, have pictures even, you know, how you do sex and all tose things...” The chairperson had to shut her up and the representative left in a hurry (quoted in *The Star*, 24th November 1999).

“A luta continua!” I sing to the tune of *Ring-a-ring-a-rosie*, as I run my last cold bath of the day.

Slowly I start to make an impact in my barren garden. The basil seeds that I have sown in a pot are coming up. I have cowdung delivered to build up the poor soil. The heap of dung attracts the flies. I hang an eco-friendly fly-trap in a tree. I stick iron rods into every mole hill and place an empty glass Coke bottle upside down onto each. The vibrations as the bottle is moved on the rod by the wind keep the moles away. This I learn from Birgit von der Vogelweide, a retired German botanist, who lives across the road. She regularly comes round to my house bearing flowers, bunches of herbs, several surreal chameleons from her garden. I fish for information concerning the neighbours.

"A small minded buch", she says. "Middle middle class". She leans forward confidentially: "There is nothing they fear more that a woman living by herself." As she leaves she points to my windows "you have to put in bars, you know," she says. "the old widow, who lived here, refused point blank. She used to say "When it is one's time, it is one's time".

Is it my time?
My gardener gives me six rose bushes from his home nursery.

"To console you", he says, "and don't worry we'll green it up for you here!"

He helps me plant the daylilies, that I have brought down with me, in their new places. My brother puts in a irrigation system that soaks the place within minutes. My sister hangs curtains in the lounge. Huge woolly rolls of pink fibreglass insulation material are stacked in my passage. The roof is being insulated tomorrow and the man from Coolvent is coming to install a split unit air-conditioning for my study.
As I write this, the measurements are finally being taken for the burglar bars. I offer the measurer a glass of cold tea.

"Hmm" he says sipping it. "This is rather good. What is it called? Where do you buy it?"

"At the Spar" I say "San Benedetto. Iced tea. Imported from Italy. The local tea was taken from the shelves after people started falling ill. Some acid apparently fell into it".

"This country is going to the dogs", the man mumbles. "Th s is boody dark Africa all over again".

Il faut cultiver notre jardin I say.

"Excuse me?" he says.

"Voltaire" I say "The Enlightenment".

"The what?"

"Never mind," I say. "We must just do it. Whatever the cost. With pop rivets. Nothing less. So we can sleep easy".

"I agree," he says, "one can't be too careful these days. What does your husband do, by the way?"

1 Breytenbach, Breyten: *Brief uit die Vreemde aan Slagter. Aan Balthazar* (Letter from Abroad to the Butcher. Dedicated Balthazar. This refers to the first name of B. J. Vorster), from the collection Skryt. Poetry International Serie First Impression 1972 Meulenhoff.
2 Adam Small, coloured poet and intellectual, known for his virulent and lyrical protest poetry against the Apartheid goverment in the sixties.
3 Afrikaner: denotation adopted by first free-lease holders in the Dutch colony of the Cape in the seventeenth century. Later appropriated by the nationalist Government as a mobilising and discriminating term for white Afrikaans-speaking people.
4 Schama, S.: *The Embarrassment of Riches*. Fontana Press, 1991.

Mia Couto

African issues: fleeting identities

>I I am a white African writer. The lack of old roots in the place where I live plays against me. I have the same things against me as the whale has in the stomach of the ocean: the price of being something new. Being a border creature favours me: between races, cultures, religions; between the universes of the oral and the written. And as I am Mozambican, another border exists: that between the West and the East.
I am a biologist and during my fieldwork I often visit rural areas in Mozambique where very few exchanges between worlds take place. I saw a group of youngsters in a village once discussing if I was "black" or not. The debate seemed strange. My race is obvious, my skin colour, the colour of my hair and eyes leave no room for doubt. I could be Swedish in Sweden. What were they really discussing? The fact is that there is no word for "white" in the language spoken in that region. There isn't even a word to name another race, in the biological sense. It seems that "mulungo" is used to refer to white people. But this word is used flexibly in a wide range of applications: it covers blacks, mulattos and Indians who act like whites. "Mulandi" seems to be what we know as a "black person". But "mulandis" can be other people, people who belong to other races but whose behaviour is seen always as native. Therefore, for the youngsters of that village, the presence of a white person who spoke the local language and who behaved in a certain way made them doubt.
The aim of this short text is precisely to underline the ambiguity of identities, and in this case, of African identities.

>II First of all, the obsession with classifying what is and what is not African, starts in Europe. Disciplines such as ethnography or anthropology analyzed these perceptions and up until recently, aimed to identify essences instead of processes. Those who defined these identities resembled sailors of the 16th century: some were anxious to baptize territories that had already been baptized a long time before; others were in a hurry to categorize populations whose profiles they didn't even know themselves: tribes, ethnic groups, clans...

>III Think, for example, of the cultural production of the African peoples. Instead of valuing the diversity of this production and seeing a book as a cultural product, literary appreciation has been replaced by a more or less ethnographic view. The question is, how far is this author really African? No one knows exactly what to be "authentically African" really means. But the book and the author still have to go through this test of identity. Or of a certain conception of identity.
An African writer faces a demand never made of a European or an American. He is obliged to prove his authenticity. He is asked up to what point he is ethnically genuine. Nobody questions how far José Saramago represents the Lusitanian culture. It is irrelevant to know if James Joyce fitted into the cultural pattern of this or that European ethnic group.
Why should African authors have to show their cultural passports? This happens because it is still believed that their cultural production belongs to the domain of ethnology or anthropology. They are not producing literature; they are producing a transgression of what is known to be traditionally African.

>IV I remember something that happened to me recently. I was appointed member of a jury to choose a new national anthem. The political changes of the past decade had raised doubts about the anthem chosen on Independence in 1975. A first competition was held but produced nothing of any quality. It was decided to hold a second public competition with the idea of mobilising talented people at all levels. I knew that there was a well-known musician living in a fishing community. I went to talk to him, to encourage him to come up with a new piece. The man didn't speak Portuguese but only one of the many languages that I do not speak. So I needed an interpreter. The difficulties were enormous. Words to refer to concepts such as Nation, Anthem, Constitution, Republic, did not exist in the language he spoke. The old musician surprised us suddenly by asking:

"Why do we need all this?"

"All this? What do you mean?"

"All this. A flag, an anthem, a nation...".

I don't think I could have explained it to him convincingly. Happily, the translator took the initiative.

>IV Obviously I am not questioning our incursion into a certain type of modernity. I am questioning the historicity and the relativity of categories and concepts. Race, nation and literature are all concepts closely related to the history of Western philosophy. In the 18th and 19th centuries connections were established in Euro-American thought between race and nationality and between nation and literature. Nowadays, our writers –the national writers– write, with only a few exceptions, in Portuguese. This means that they stand in the nation (the biological, natural entity) and their mind is in the realm of the State (the human entity, the artifice of modernity). Now, this placement in the territory of the other –whose values we all grew up with, and through which we became assimilated to this cultural race to which I belong– brings both a feeling of identification and of inequality.
We will belong to the family of nations. We have an anthem and a flag. We are proud to use our right to our own name. Much blood was spilled before we could enjoy our right to citizenship. But despite all this, we may have a name, but we do not have individuality, we are "Africans". As if everything were the same within this plural term. As if Africa were an easy and simple matter which could fit into this one word. As if Africa did not have the right to diversity and to its own multiculturalism. This reductionist identity (the way "Africans" are seen) is dangerous because in theoretical terms it is false and in practical terms, unproductive. How far does this identification –usually thought of in terms of race– give us courage and stimulate us to find practical and innovative solutions? These concepts of race –"black", "white", "African"– are inventions of European domination. The "white man" invented the "black man" in order to dominate him better. What is known today as "Africa" is the result

of European racist invention. The Africans adopted this same concept without questioning it from a historical point of view. Most of us haven't the slightest idea of how much the concepts we are now working with are products of ideology, presuppositions invisibly built upon by History.
I almost feel like the musician-fisherman. I don't even know why we have to think in these terms: nation or national identity. These concepts were generated by History: nations must present themselves in the ceremony of the world with these identifying robes. There is no way we can dodge the rules of this game. But it would be worthwhile to apply some originality to these concepts and to assimilate them according to the rhythm of our own needs.
The absence of nation was imposed on us by colonialism; the urgency for it is being imposed on us by neo-colonialism. But it is not only a question of hegemonic impositions from outside. African élites conceived the idea of nation as a form of resistance against foreign domination. It is a paradox that, at the same time, nationhood enables these élites to become better integrated into the world system which allows them to continue to be privileged social groups.

>VI Similar ambiguities exist when one tries to locate what is authentically African in rural tradition. As if the modernity that the African people are inventing is not in itself African. This narrow-minded and restrictive way of conceiving what is genuine is possibly one of the main reasons why literature produced in Africa is looked on with distrust. Literature is on the side of modernity.
The opposition between what is traditional –seen as the pure uncontaminated side of African culture– and what is modern (where literature has its place), is, in great measure, a false contradiction. Rural imagery is also the result of exchanges between different cultural worlds. What is considered "pure" is, in a final analysis, the result of the creation of many hybrids. The majority of young people of rural culture in my country dream of being Michael Jackson or Eddy Murphy. Above all, they dream of becoming black Americans.

>VII Senghor wrote, “Here I am, trying to forget Europe in the heart of Senegal”. The Senegalese statesman and poet was never able to forget. He was a bridge between two continents. He couldn't be anything else. To forget Europe cannot imply an elimination of the conflicts that shaped our own identities (Would we be “Africans” without colonialism?). Between that invitation to forget Europe and the dream of being American, the only way out that we can envisage is to take a step forward. African intellectuals have no need to be ashamed of wanting to mix. They do not have to correspond to the image that European myths have built. They do not lack stratagems nor symbols in order to be Africans. They are Africans, just as they are, with a soul made up of many parts, because Africa has an absolute right to modernity. Africa has the right to fully recognise the mixing of bloods that she, herself, started and that make her more diverse, and because of this, much richer.

>VIII My border situation, between cultures, does not come from being the child of Europeans. All my black Mozambican compatriots who are writers like me find themselves in the same situation of confluence. Luckily for them. The ambivalence of African intellectuals, artists and politicians should be seen as positive, an efficient mixing of bloods, a means of finding their own solutions. It is an enriching departure point in the creation of an identity which can only be conceived as dynamic and changing. To be both inside and outside is a privilege in a world in which frontiers are disappearing. To be at the same time indigenous and alien puts them in the position of a privileged visitor, the seamstress of different cultural cloths.

>IX A real identity is not to be built only by emphasising this project of nationality or “continentality” (this hazy “Africa”), but rather by questioning these concepts and epistemological presuppositions. It is not a question of opposing a justified Afro-centricity to Euro-centricity. Black arrogance is not the answer to white arrogance. The easy answers such as “affirmative action” have the same effect as racial definitions. Racism

is dangerous because it does not generate a future and is the cause of misleading and superficial alliances when the true conflicts in Africa move along a different border line which has nothing to do with race. It is necessary to escape from this trap, and the African people, who fearlessly face their belonging to a world of mixed races, are the only ones who can do it. Even though experts on Africa try to go against so-called European concepts, they are still prisoners of these concepts. Even if it is only to grant importance. Even if this importance is conceived negatively. It is not a question of finding an identity by going back in time searching for ancestral purity. The fiercest defendants of African cultural nationalism are designing houses upside-down within the context of the architecture of the Other, of what we call the West. A fetishist attitude towards customs, folklore and vernacular traditions is useless. Colonial domination invented a large part of the past and of African tradition. Ironically, some African intellectuals, wanting to negate Europe, opened their arms to some of these colonial concepts.

>X In a few lines, I have tried to pose certain questions about some misunderstandings that separate us, on one side and the other of the border of thought. As it is too late to escape from one another, we should, instead, put our memories of our mutual interdependence to work for us. We should conceive the past as the motor of the future. But not the staged version of the past with which some want to fool us. Since all pasts –as all historical times– are the result of invention, let us recreate the History of our past as the foundation of that other race we all belong to: mankind.

Moses Isegawa

Another hour, another day

Four years ago my grandfather passed away at ninety six, a ripe age for the human animal, a flash in the pan compared to the immense history of the universe. I was lucky that he kept his sanity all his life and never got tired of telling me stories of his past. He firmly believed that it was through looking at people's lives that we arrive at the more general truth about a village, a country or a continent.

Grandfather received little classroom education but because he was naturally smart, curious and hard working, he managed to fall in love with the printed word and kept educating himself all his life. At the start of the First World War, when he was ten years old, he saw his father leave home to go and fight the Germans. He never came back. The gap this loss left he filled with work.

At the start of the Second World War he was conscripted. He saw action in Ethiopia and returned at the end of the war to be part of a new world, where the position of both black and white people in Uganda had changed. White people were no longer called "God"; black people had trained guns on them, heard their cries and fired or granted them mercy. They were mortal after all. The myth of omnipotence on which most white power had been constructed was dead.

He participated in demonstrations called by organizations demanding better conditions for ex-combatants and more freedom for every Ugandan. He was fond of saying: "Don't mess with me. I fought in the biggest war in the world". Independence found him fighting for more rights and better pay for black workers.

In 1972 President Amin gave the Indians ninety days to leave Uganda. Grandfather saw it as the dislodging of the remnants of colonial middlemen and the ushering in of a new era in Uganda's politics. Up to his death he would agree that Amin had done a lot of bad things but he was behind him in getting rid of the Indians.

The biggest gift Grandfather gave his only son, my father, was education. He instilled in him a love for books, for he believed that tomorrow's wars would be fought by book knowledge. He was fond of saying: "There are two sacred places in my house: my chest of books and my head."

My father became a primary school teacher and at independence, when many positions in the civil service fell open, he left the village and went to the city to work for the National Electricity Board. He was an avid reader of books and magazines, which had a prominent place in his house. He educated his children well, sending us to boarding school where we could concentrate on our education undistracted by the chaos of Amin's regime.

As a result I grew up seeing the printed word around me. I remember many afternoons spent in my father's abandoned village house wrestling with the words on the pages of *Time* and other magazines. I would be lying if I said that I knew what the future held in store for me. It was just that there were not many things to do in the village except looking for mangoes and sugarcanes and, when one became bored, looking at the printed page trying to unlock its secrets. I loved the cat-and-mouse games with the sentences so much that I remember resolving to become a writer at fifteen.

When he was buying books my grandfather never knew that he was working towards a great moment in Uganda's literary history. Neither did my father realize that he was grooming a writer in his house. How could he when there had never been a single writer in my entire family's history? But twenty years after my resolution, I published *Abyssinian Chronicles* to world acclaim. Grandfather was ecstatic, boasting that it had all began with his books.

It is my belief that in countries like Uganda the future is still an open space waiting to be moulded by common people. In my village there is now a writer, two doctors and three teachers born and raised there. It is a great contribution to national life.

Looking at the history of the human animal, from his evolution from a single bacterium to a worm, to a bird, to a monkey, to his present form, it has been an uncertain journey, defying all predictions. Africa, the cradle of mankind, has made great strides even if some people are blinded to the same by a morbid focus on what is wrong and what is yet to be done.

They are so caught up in the instant-gratification fever of this age that they forget that all things take time.
When I look back to my small village I can't but be filled with pride and confidence in the future. I am proud because my family invested in a vague entity called education and was rewarded with a writer. I am confident because the human animal has to push on into tomorrow whatever happens. It is not that the future belongs exclusively to those with nuclear missiles and space ships. Everybody who is alive is part of the future, that blind rush for another breath, another minute, another hour, another day.
Prosperity, the shaky yardstick by which many measure tomorrow, is but a recent invention. Just sixty years ago the world was caught up in the savagery of the Second World War. Few could predict a prosperous future, but everybody knew Europe would survive. Europe has had its share of war, poverty, disease and deprivation. Africa is going through its time of war, poverty and deprivation. War is something Africa will have to learn to control just as Europe has learned to control its war-like instincts in the name of the common good. The trick could be for Africa to start making weapons instead of importing them. "Strong nations don't easily fight each other", my grandfather used to say. But all that is speculation. What I know for sure is that, unlike my grandfather, my father and myself, Africa is not going to disappear from the map of the world. It has been marching on for billions of years. It will always be there living for another minute, another hour, another day. Its eternal duty.

November 2004

Nawal el Saadawi

In celebration of my African roots

My paternal grandfather had a dark skin. His name was Habash and habash in Arabic means “a man from Abyssinia”. He was born in the midst of forest trees on the shores of Lake Victoria Nyanza. From here the long voyage of the river Nile begins, from here he travelled to Abyssinia. Was he trying to discover the course of the Nile? Did he travel alone, and how old was he? When I used to ask my grandmother her thoughts seemed to stray, and her eyes would no longer be looking at me. “No –she would say– he was not alone. His mother was with him all the way. He was only a boy in those days, strong and sturdy, but not yest seasoned enough to reach the plateaus of Abyssina on his own. It is the women in our family who have always known the way”.

A few years went by. He grew older and so did she. One day she said to him it's time to leave: “We must travel north, to where the land is fertile and grows more food”. They gathered their few belongings then went to sep. When he woke up in the morning she was no longer there. He waited all day but she did not come back, so he understtod that from now on he would travel alone, follow the Nile right down to a fertile land. And that is how he came to the village of Kafr Tahla and founded the family into which I was born.

My father inherited my great grand father's skin and so did I. He was proud to be an African. When i was a child he would say to me: “Do not listen to the allies of British and French colonialism when they say that Egypt is a part of Europe, and that only the sea lies in between. It is the colonialists who separated Africa into North and South, into White and Black, or Sub Saharan Africa. Divide and rule that is what those who have the power and the money always do. They carved up the continent between themselves, drew the borders of countries to suit their needs, cut into tribes and families, into grazing lands and villages. For years they have plundered its natural wealth, distorted its natural life, its beauty”.

My father's óbice talks to me from the inner depths of my woman's body. It speaks of violation, a word well known to women like me, of a violated continent, cut to pieces, struggling to survive, despite every thing.

People sep asking me what is your "identity". It is a question which people form the North like to address to people form the South like me. I say: "I am African". "African?", they say. Then comes the next question. "From what African country do you come?" I say: "From Egypt" as I pronounce the name I can see their eyes open wide in surprise, before they ask "But is Egypt a part of Africa?!".
Since the British occupation in 1882, the ruling class in Egypt and its intellectuals, started to turn their hearts and minds towards the North, to Europe, and their backs, towards Africa and its peoples, towards their real selves, their history and their experience. They became ashamed of their dark skin, of their Egyptian Arabic language, so rich in words and intonation. From then on they went to foreign schools. Arabic bacame the language of the poor, of maids and servants, of workers and peasants, of ignorant and illiterate people.
When I was a child my maternal aunts tried conceal the dark colour of my skin with pastes and powders, to straighten my kinky hair with hot irons, so that it would become smooth and silky.
Deep incide me I nurtured a love for my brown complexión, for the colour of silt carried down by the nile from Abyssinia, for my kinky hair, I had to rebel against the rules and restrictions forced upon me by my family and my teachers, to refuse their values, and their ways of seeing things.
Later on in high school, and in the university, I participated in strikes and demonstrations against the British and the king.
On the 23rd of July 1952 the king was obligated to leave the country after the "Free Officers" came to power. In November 1956 the last British soldiers wer evacuated after the armies of Britain, france and Israel had invaded Egypt. Under the regime of Nasser Egypt started to strengthen its links with African countries and peoples. This did not last very long. In 1970 Anwar El-Sadat came to power and Egypt became a part of a reinvented Middle East which included the Arab Gulf States, Israel, and Turkey.
I sep asking myself: this term Middle East, what does it mean? Middle to whom and East to whom? To the West? But why should the West decide

the geopolitical position to which I belong? Why should I accept ethnocentric terms that continue to decide my place in the world? I refuse to be dependent, to have my identity or my name, my present or my future decide by the West. I am opposed to the hierarchies of money and power, of patriarchy, and class of religión, and race. Why should the rulers in the West draw my frontiers, and my maps, thell me who I am, how to think, and see, and act?

When I describe England as "Middle West" or the United States of America as "Far West" people look at me, as though I should be locked Hawai in a safe place (this is the term used by Sadat when he decided to imprison the opposition in September 1981, and sent me off to the women's penitentiary north of Cairo). Yet that is exactly where they are placed in relation to my country.

But it is economic and military power that decides for us who we are, and where we stand, it is neither justice nor the logic of the mind and heart. It is small minorities who own nuclear power and banks. They control the class patriarchal system, rule over the global market. They are changing the world into an electronic, laser, fibre optic, inhuman space, where people can starve, or die, or wast Hawai as we watch on a televisión screen. It is the same system which changes a woman's name when she marries and makes Egypt a part of the Middle East together with Israel and Turkey.

Since the imperialists discovered Africa, the continent where smiles still shine on dark faces, and where people teach others how to dance has been hanged form a source of economic and cultural wealth, into dismembered starving, warring states with corrupt rulers who are often no more than brutal agents of transnational corporations. The hundreds of ethnic groups which lived in harmony before the "white man" started to explore the rivers and green forests of Africa have found ghemselves engaged in civil or border wars, in mass massacres. Peaceful men, women and children are killed in thousands by armies, militia, or mercenary force recruited and armed to serve the interests of trasnational corporations based in the United States of America, France,

England, Belgium, Germany or Switzerland. The armed struggles which have broken out beween Eritrea and Etiopía, in Rwanda and Burundi, in Angola, in Zaire (the democratic Republic of Congo), in Liberia and Sieira Leone, in Nigeria, in Algeria, in the sudan, on the surface appear as tribal, ethnic, or religious struggles. But venid each one of them lies the legacy of colonialism and imperialism, the transnatinal corporations trading in arms, oil, cobalt, zinc, coppr, and other minerals, as well as in diamonds and gold or in plantations growing cocoa, coffee, cloves and tea.
The infinite minority who rule over the transnational corporations in the United States, Europe and Japan cannot maintain their strong hold over Africa, and exploit its peoples, decimate them by hunger, war, aids and other diseases unless they continne to fight one another, unless they find ways of fuelling the ethnic struggles which they themselves started during the centuries of mercantile, and colonial rule, unless they use religious strife as a weapon to disipate the constructive energies of people and lead them astray into unbridled destruction of one another, into the backwardness and fanatism of the Dark Ages.
In my own life I have known what it is to struggle against the unjust system imposed on me and my sisters by male domination, and imposed on our people by colonial and neo-colonial rule, and by local rulers who for a share in the spoils are prepared to ally themselves with foreign exploiters. My father who was a man of integrity and a respected member of the educations community in Egypt was obliged to live and teach for then long years in a small district town called Menouf, because in 1936 he had dared to lead a demnstratiion of students from the school in which he was teaching to protest against British colonial rule and the king. My husband (Sherif Hetata) spent fourteen years in prison doind hard labour because he joined a left wing political party called “the Democratic Movement for National Liberation”. I too did a stint in prison because I opposed president Sadat’s submission to the neo-colonial polices of the United States, to neo-leberal open door policies which increased the gap between the rich and the poor, encouraged religious fundamentalism at the expense of democratic national and liberal forces

in the country, made life difficult for women both economically and socially, and submitted the future of the Palestinian and Arab people to American and Israeli hegemonic interests.

Prison, opresión,a nd even death have been the fate of many intellectuals and democrats in Egypt and the other countries of Africa, when they expressed opposition to the colonial and neo-colonial powers and their local allies. Amongst the thousands of brave men and women who suffered are writers like Ngugi Wa Thiongo, who fled from Kenya, from the persecutions of Arap Moi and others, and Ama Ata Aido the Ghanian woman writer who had to leave her home country and now lives and teaches at a university in the States. I have met Ama Ata Aido a number of times. The last one was during the month of August 1999, at the Internatinal Book Fair held in Harare, the capital of Zimbabwe. Immediately before the Fair a women's writers conference was convened and many women writers came to Harare from all parts of Africa to participate in the conference and attend the Fair. One of these women writers objected to my presence in the conference maintaining that Egypt and the Arab countries of North Africa did not belong to the continent of Africa . To support her contention she quoted from a book by a jamaican woman critic living in England who had composed an anthology of African women writers under the title *Daughters of Africa*. In this anthology she had not included any of the women writers who belonged to the countries of North Africa namely Morocco, Algeria, mauritania, tunisia, Libya and Egypt. This divide between North and Sub Saharan Africa was created by colonialism and perpetuated by the local ruling regimes in these countries, so that on both sides of the divide the antagonism between black and fair skinned continues. Men and women are affected by the ideas and values of the colonialists and thinkers in Africa often insist that North Africans (Arabs) are not African even if they live on the same continent, even if Arabic is one of the languages spoken and written in a number of its countries like Somalia, the Sudan, Erytria, Ethiopia etc..., even though North African countries are members fo the Organization of African Unity.

While in Harare I noticed that I was the only Arab woman writer who had been invited to the conference, an so when my turn came to speak i drew the attention of the partipats to this tendency and expressed the hope that the organizers of future conferences in Africa would not commit the same error. But a few months later I had to repeat the same thing in Asmara, where I was attending a conference during January 2000, entitled "Against All Odds: African Languages and Linguistics towards the Future".
I was also struck by the way in which even the most prominent speakers failed to make the link between culture and economics failed to realiza that a culture, a language, whithout material support is doomed to die out sooner or later, failed to realize that the neo-colonialist thinkers make long sermons about their respect for culture, for cultural and religious diversity, for what they call specificity, authentic identity and multiculturalism, and yet watch with placid eyes the economic genocide to which the peoples of Africa are being exposed, failed to see that the poor all over the world including those in the rich industrial countries need work and food as well as culture in order to live as human beings.
I wonder whether this tendency in African conferences is not partly a result of the fact that almost all of them are organized and funded with substantial contributions form American or European institutions of agencies.
My relationship with Africa is a physical feeling, almost organic. I feel my rotos striking deep south to the source of the Nile as it surges through a narrow opening in Lake Victoria Nyanza close to the small twn of Jindja to form one of the two rivers which unite in Omdurman to become the Nil. My body comes from the red earth of Uganda, of Ethiopia, of the Sudan. It is born, nourished, made to stand, to walk, to live on the silt of the Nile. I can smell the wss, the forest trees, the bulrushes that surround it on either side. I lived in Addis Abeba during 1979 when I worked with the Economic Commission for Africa in the United Nations. I visited Uganda, slept in Kampala, rode a bus to Jindja through the green forests of that beautiful land when Idi Amin instilled fear in the heearts of his people and depended on his soldiers to rule the land.

During the time I worked with the ECA I visited many African countries and participated with my sisters in Africa in establishing the African Women's Association for Research and Development (AWARD, Dakar, 1979). In Harare (1985) we established the African Women's Writers Association and we gathered again in the same city during 1999 to strengthen our network.
Africa is a suffering continent, a victim of capitalist globalization, which is being rapidly marginalized and reduced to the status of a fourth world, loaded with a foreign debt of more than 350 milliard dollars, crippled with hunger, war and disease. Yet I was amazed to meet so many wonderful men and women writers, thinkers, and intellectuals. They were full of an irrepresible joy and laughter, of a spontaneity not yet spoiled by the distorted use of a technology imposed by a global capitalism, seeking to devour and absorb all productive human forces in the service of a race for profit, of unbridled accumulation at the expense of basic human rights. Milliards of people, pay the price to maintain the privileged few, to ensure a progress which is made only by riding rough shod over the bodies of men and women and children allover the world.
We cannot resist this global exploitations except by unifying the efforts of women and men, of children and youth in all parts of the world, by a democratic process of globalizaicn from below. Perhaps the demonstrations is Seattle (November–December 1999) and other similar events in Europe, have shown the way, are the beginning of a long journey the direction of which will become clearer as we move forward. The real challenge to the capitalist patriachal system and its institutions (the World Trade Organization, the World Bank, the IMF and others) has started and should continue globally and locally. There are many difficulties not the least of which is the diversity and the contradictions inherent in the human race, the problems caused by class and religión, gender and race, by the legacy of history, of time and place, of upbringing and social difference. But the democratic mobilization of peoples must find new ways to acomódate differences in the search for unity amongst peoples, for unity is the only way to deal with the economic, technologiacl

and military might of the global few, and to counter a growing monopoly of knowledge and of the media in the hands.

In this movement for globalization from below, intellectuals fo Africa, women and men, writers, teachers, journalists, film makers, scientists, technicians, professionals, have an important role to play. They must stand on the side of their peoples, and not become neo-orientalists whose role is to progagate the values, theories and ideas of post-modernism, of the global few. They must not become dark skinned, missionaries of a capitalist system that servers the five hundred transnational corporations and the seven industrial countries which control eighty per cent of the production and wealth of the world. They should not speak the language of división, of ethnicity and religion and race, of culture divorced form the conomy which means no culture at all, of unbridled individualism and competition, where competition works only to the advantage of a few, of the death of comunal initiative and effort, of Free Trade instead of Fair Trade, of Aid and consumption instead of production and equal exchange, of privilege instead of justice for all women and men of the world. The global capitalists have learnt the art of buying dark skinned men and women to serve as the ideologists of the end of history, the clash of civilizations and other similar theories, so that they continue to rule, of a post-modern thought which emphasizes identity politics and difference aginst unity, helplessness against resistance, and proclaims the end of representation, organization and emanipatory movements.

We need thinkers who are fighters who are thinkers. We need women and men authors who live what they write and write what they live. We need to produce what we eat and eat what we produce for we live on one of the most fertile and rich continents of the world.

But now inspite of all the difficulties, I feel that people everywhere are once more on the move.

Cairo, Egypt, 26 February 2000

Nuruddin Farah

Millennium text

A millennium is too long a period for anyone to reduce it to a tableau vivant at once dramatic and representational. Even so, I believe that we should all try to define what the millennium means to us. For my part, I will approach it from the perspective of a Somali, born into the oral tradition, and will seek out the wisdom of a fabulist and fellow countryman, Sheeko Xariir (in Somali, "the teller of silky tales").

It's related that whilst on a soul-searching journey, Sheeko Xariir came upon a road with so many trajectories that he had difficulty choosing which tack to take. A fabulist, he lighted upon a most original idea, that of rolling up all the roads into one giant road, and then wearingthem round his wais, as a conjurer might wear a snake round his neck, unafraid. And he walked, and walked and walked, remaining committed to reaching the one giant road in the end. Every now and then he would unfold the next roll, then the one after that and so on and so forth, until he achieved the most impossible feat imaginatively in a way of which only a fabulist was capable. Spurred, in part, by the giant need to come to terms with the many-sidedness of a viewpoint, I feel like the fabulist of years gone. For I too have a number of trajectories to choose from, considering where I've ended up, here in the Cittá di Capo, where the millennium will eventually catch up with me. From where I am, the millennium looks like a painting with great promise, a painting hung askew.

Viewed from this end, this has been a rogue millennium insofar as a large number of people are concerned, in which millions have been turned into, and defined as, sub-humans by the very nature of who we've become. Large segments of world's population were dispossessed of their land, made dysfunctional, colonized, or put into concentration camps and exterminated, in the name of master theories of morality, theories organized around the idea of gender, race or religion. The theories were expounded at lenght in books, a few of them sacred, a great many of them profane. Recently manumitted from one sort of bondage or another, we are alive to the detritus of so much injustice carried out on the sanction of these Sacred Texts or on the basis of the secular sciences. Now that the second millennium has a year or less to go, I ask myself, can one forgive a wrong committed but not owned up, a wrong not openly admitted to?

Meanwhile, in the grand architecture of death and life, Sheeko Xariir millennial idea-constructs revolve around the thinking that a thing not yet born is alive with a millennium of possibilities germane to the making of yetanother book of fables. Whereupon I reiterate that the present millennium was barely a century old when a tide of crusading fervours pitted the Ahlul-Kitaab (in Arabic, "people of the Book") against one another, unleashing centuries of attrition, and creating generations of friction between Muslims and Christians. Jerusalem was the bone of contention in 1095, the aim of the Christian military expedition being to recover the Holy Sepulchre from Muslim hands. The more things change, the more they remain the same, would you not agree?

If I'm obsessed with fables, it's because I hold the view that it is through them that one attains a better sense of the current shenanigans about the new millennium. However, I cannot think of a more appropriate fabulist to re-read than Italo Calvino, a giant among contemporary European novelists, who chose the title *Six Memos for the Next Millennium* for a series of talks meant to be delivered as the 1985 Charles Eliot Norton Lectures at Harvard University. I am now interested not so much in the sad fact that he died before his imminent departure to the US to give them as I am in a throw-away gem of a remark buried in a brief introduction to the published lectures.

According to him, this "has been the millennium of the book, in that it has seen the object we call a book take on the form familiar to us". In a nutshell, what sets this millennium apart from the previous ones has been the revolutionary changes which are to do with the making of the book, designed to serve as an instrument of communication and of knowledge. Never mind the speculation current among post-industrial societies that "books" will become outmoded as technological advances threaten their very existence. But when you get down to why "books" are important, it is this: they contain portable "knowledge", communicated in written form, and disseminate in every "literate" society. I doubt that Calvino thought about Alfred Tennyson's exquisite lines, "Thy feet, millenniums

hence, be set in midst of knowledge!", when he wrote his lectures, given that in Tennyson's days, "millennium" meant a period of happiness and benign government! To Calvino, "books" and the explorative archeology of knowledge through them distinguish thi milennium from the others preceding it.
A pity we cannot agree on wheter the millenrium begins on January 1st, 2000 or January 1st, 2001. Anyhow, it is apparent that, in its self-referential variants, the term itself is steeped in controversy, not only about when it will dawn, but also for whom. Besides, we cannot help thinking that Christians assume that the bells of the millennium will also toll for the Muslims, the Hindu, the Buddhist, and the animist at the same time as it does for them. But does it? Here in Cape Town, we are inundated wih the combined sell-by-date of the millennium as it enters into a religious pact with Christmas. My wife and I have no less than eleven members of her family arriving to spend Christmas with us, because, among other distinguishing characteristics, Cape Town has been designated as The City of the Millennium City! Christmas, the New Year and the Millennium do not mean the same things for my (Muslim) side of the family!
A people of the book, my Muslim side of the family was introduced to the larger world via Arabic, a tongue referred to by its native speakers as "the Language of the Book". The idea of alfabetic symbols representing the sounds we make so fascinated me on my first day at the Quranic School that I refused to come home. We had our indigenous form of learning the Arabic alphabet, in a sort of mnemonic verse we chanted, now separetely, now together. What I didn't know, then, was that the first chapter revealed to the Prophet was contained in the divine command, "Iqra!" meaning "Read!". It strucks me as ominously *déjá vu* on coming across the first sentence: "This is a book" in our English language textbook; this was followed by "This is a pen". I felt I was a child of a second millennium, the millennium of the Book!
As with book, so with the millennium: a regenerations of sorts. All the same the regenrative act that I have in mind is not to be found in the millennium about to daw, but in the Islamic notion of *hegira* (in Arabic,

“emigration”, or “flight from persecution”), upon which we base the Muslim calendar. To me, this makes a great deal more sense, because the *hegira* mirrors my people’s current condition, exiles in flight. Mark you, we are not so much in flight from a country with a defined phisicality as we are feeling from states of mind, or rather aspects of ourselves to which we are unable to reconcile ourselves.

As Africans too, our current condition is equally reflected in the Hegira, mirrored as it is in opur agitated period of flux, our contrition alternating with states of self-doubt. Viewed from the prospective of a secularist, you would agree that the terrible things have been done to a great number of us during the past one thousands years, in the name of the People of the Book. Given that we have a lot of catching-up to do, I ask, does the millennium begin for everybody at the same time, no matter who we are: Africans, communities of the Hindu faith, or Buddhists, or of the animist faith. There is a nebulous imprecision about these questions, and this is significant. And I raise them in view of the fact that we do not wish those who’ve been in the driving-seat of the millennium to imposing their worldview on us.

Dates, and how we locate them in our memory, or rather history, are constantly being reinterpreted. After all we do not see dates as mere numbers placed in a given order, but as points of reference with intricate subjective contexts. I’ve had to revise my understadning of the universe ever since first going to school, and becoming aquainted with The Book. I am sure that many others have had to do similar things. Dates and the “personalities” who qualified the books or who are qualified by them have always been questioned, albeit more scientifically in the recent past. Sacred texts aside, ask me what Christopher Columbus represents, and my answer ought to dissent from the description I encountered in my history reader at school. To a child growing up and going to school in the fifties, he was described as a discoverer of a continent. Over the years, I’ve had to revise my views about many of the things I was taught, and have had to challenge a great number of the knowledge imparted to me as an adult about Cecil Rhodes, Lugard, Kitchener, the Mahdi of the Sudan, the so-called “Mad Mullah” of Somalia. These radical self-appraisals have helped us determine where the contested sites are, enabling us to revisit our memories, and comparing ours as victims with the memories of the perpetretors of the crimes. Even so, dates tend to moonlight for the singularly famous and the great to such an extent we remember 1492 as Columbu's day, and not as the day n which the natives of a continent were dispossessed of their way of li-e.

I'm not speaking so much about the acrimonious histories between the colonized and the colonizers as much I am talking about dates and books. In the Bermudan triangle of treasure-hunting history, some of us who belong to the oral tradition have neither "made" our myths into Sacred Books nor committed the treasure of our oral culture into written formats, or created museums, or built libraries in homage to our memories. But we have insitutions of memory. Sadly, the custodians of our cultures are dying out, and we need must invest in the making of books for our memory to survive and serve.

Colours picking up other colours in a room: that's what centuries are. Fettered with chains of our making, we are locked into ou- sallow history, the ashen hue of subjective understanding of our beginnings, privileging ours over other peoples' memory. Thanks to the books, we are living in historic times, in which we enter into disagreements without crossing swords. In future, it is my hope that we will tell the whole and true story of the millennium in as many tongues as there are, no longer remaining history's victims, and no longer relying on reciting a litany of woes committed against us in the past. Only then we will the new millennium begin for us too. Books are the contact zone, if humanity is to be saved from its self-destruction.

In the next millennium the world will have become a polyglot, and books will have been the languages we've either learnt or are going to learn: as the future steals in upon us as shadow do, with the qu et of a vowel having the potential of a guttural sound. These babble of languages will have been made into an ocean of stories, and eventually into the one book that will tell all the stories, the story of our humanity!

There will have been justice for all: in books!

Pepetela

An ambiguous century

Whoever attempts to analyse the 20th century in Africa through the eyes of an Angolan will have very mixed feelings and will be puzzled on more than one account. Firstly it has to be said that it is practically impossible to evaluate the continent as a whole, because of the diversity of situations that exists. I will start by leaving to one side what is known as North Africa, an area that has ancient links with Mediterranean civilizations and where some of exceptional importance were born, such as the Egypt of the Pharaohs and Carthage. I will concentrate on what is generally known as Black Africa. Here also the differences amongst civilizations are so great that the mosaic becomes extremely complicated. Therefore I will narrow down my study even more and speak only of the former Portuguese colonies. And even then we will see that the processes that these colonies went through differed according to the relative economic importance of the territories and their location. Every case is different and there is little point in trying to see things as a whole. I will try to analyse the century as Angola experienced it, even though I may need to make comparisons with other neighbouring processes. Finally, I will attempt to find a way to outline a perspective for the 21st century, a generalisation for the whole continent.
Europeans began colonising different regions of the black continent according to their own interests and the balance of power at the time. Generally the19th century is known as the period of colonisation. However, there are some exceptions such as Angola and South Africa, where Europeans had settled earlier. If we look at the processes in more detail, we can say that the real colonisation of Africa, especially of the area to the south of the Sahara, took place during the 20th century after the Berlin Conference, which divided the region into two parts to satisfy the European powers' voracious appetite for colonies. Therefore, colonisation and decolonisation belong to the 20th century.
One could say that, in Angola, the process of colonisation starts in 1575 with the foundation of the city of Luanda. In my opinion, it is incorrect to use the term "colonisation" for an earlier period, when referring to the relationship between the Portuguese Crown and the Kingdom of the

Congo, the region in the north of what is now Angola. In the century prior to the foundation of Luanda, the Portuguese interfered greatly in the affairs of the Congo through political pressures and manoeuvres, Catholic evangelisation, and the involvement of the local potentates in the slave trade, thus causing far-reaching changes in social relations and family structures. It was not, strictly speaking, colonisation because the political and social structures of the Kingdom were autonomous even though the influences they received claimed to be "civilizing".

Military conquests and the establishment of settlements took place along the Angolan and Congo coasts during the following centuries. Inland invasions were carried out along two routes perpendicular to the coast, crucial as a base for the slave trade, which in turn was an essential part of the Portuguese project for Brazil. However, the colonisation of the whole territory took place in the 20th century, even if it consisted of only a small part of the population spread over a vast area that had little importance at the time. I would add that, in my opinion, if we want to specify a decade, we could say that the 20th century began in Angola around 1880. I will justify this statement gradually, since all statements require their time. The same thing happens with mangoes; they won't ripen any quicker if you wait under the tree.

As I mentioned before, with the exception of Ethiopia, Liberia and a few other countries, which followed their own trajectories, the 20th century is that of colonisation and de-colonisation. This is the case of Angola, despite the fact that the first steps were taken a long time before, though consisting only of an unsystematic occupation of some coastal areas and narrow inland strips with limited economic and human resources, leaving the forest for the hunting of slaves and ivory. Nevertheless, the idea of autonomy and emancipation from European power starts to unfold in the 19th century.

Because the Portuguese colonisers had very limited economic and human resources, they were forced to allow the creation of a strong middle class in the colony. This social class consisted of mestizos, some blacks and some whites, who had been born in Angola, and guaranteed the functioning of a large part of the inland trade, of the

public administration and of the subaltern military leadership. It was a mixture of European cultures and those of traditional African societies, and spoke Portuguese. Here was generated an intellectual élite which was especially prominent in the journalism of the last quarter of the 19th century. Dozens of newspapers, some bilingual, some in Portuguese, were edited and then shut down by governmental imposition and censorship. This élite preached the ideas of the French Revolution, criticising colonialism because it paid little attention to territorial development, and censoring the racism of the authorities against the Africans, even to the point of actually demanding the emancipation of these peoples. Nevertheless, their attitude towards the occupation of the inland kingdoms was ambiguous since they considered these peoples to be barbarians in urgent need of civilisation, *manu militari*, if need be. So generally they approved of the operations carried out by the colonial army against the independent peoples, as a means of integrating them into the colony. This first group of Angolans had a privileged position if we compare it to that of the great mass of African people spread throughout the country. At the same time, nevertheless, they felt that their rights were restricted by the Portuguese. In this situation, these early Angolans were the first to be conscious of some sort of identity of their own.
This was the cradle of the future nation and of the future nationalist sentiment that would give rise to the armed liberation movements of the second half of the 20th century. This is why I situate the birth of the 20th century, conceived as the century of national liberation, in 1880, when that intellectual élite, frequently facing court proceedings, fought with their writing to shake off the heavy yoke of the colonisation that imposed underdevelopment. They fought for an emancipation that included the badly-administered inland territories, which were practically ignored by the decadent Portuguese crown. The appearance of an intellectual élite of such quality, in a territory administered by the least advanced colonising power that Europe had produced, must have been a unique case in the Africa of that time.
The first half of the 20th century saw the destruction of the dreams of this élite. Not only was their right to political and literary intervention

decimated but the economic status of the social class they came from was eroded. As a result of the Berlin Treaty, the colonising metropolises were obliged to administrate and militarily occupy the territories that they claimed a right to. They started in the eastern part of Angola, with the hurried and almost chaotic arrival of Portuguese settlers to fill empty posts. For lack of better candidates, many common law criminals and others condemned to exile for political or religious "crimes" were deported to Angola to live alongside illiterate farmers who had asked to be sent in the hope of improving their standards of living. This mass of people, uneducated and in some cases with the lowest possible moral principles, began to compete for administrative posts and to sack the Angolans who had been occupying these positions of subsidiary authority for many years. The same thing happened with commercial and military posts. The middle class, which could now be called truly Angolan, was not only ousted from its financial means of subsistence but was also obliged to abandon its place in the coastal cities. The people were forced out to the miserable periphery, leaving the centre of the cities to the colonisers. This process accelerated dramatically when the dictator Salazar came to power in Portugal, after the *coup d'état* in 1926.

In the 1930s and especially the 40s, therefore, the Angolan élites gradually moved away from any idea of colonial assimilation. During that same period, the conditions of forced labour of the population in the interior worsened. These people were obliged to work in the building of roads, on coffee plantations or in the diamond mines for practically no wage. The policy that systematically destroyed the traditional power structures had been rehearsed for centuries on the coast and was now going inland. This struck a contrast with the English system of colonisation in which those power centres were maintained and used as intermediaries for their own sovereignty, while they educated the children of the local potentates with the idea of forming a more modern élite, well-disposed to obeying the British Empire. In the case of the Portuguese, they were not in the slightest bit concerned about educating the heirs to the thrones which had been independent until shortly before, precisely because they wanted to eliminate centres of alternative power, even

those that were dependant. In the interior, only the Christian missions opened schools for the Africans, closely watched over by distrustful agents of the administration, who preferred the "indigenous" people to be kept well away from any technology.
The policy of continuous raids that was applied in the urbanized and European coastal region, as well as in the interior, which was subject only to military rule, generated a deep-seated hatred of the colonial system. This became evident after the Second World War with the appearance of various, and often discordant, independence movements, carried along on the wave of resistance inspired by the example of Gandhi and his refusal to submit. It is at the end of the fifties in Angola when the movements that were born under the cover of cultural groups or associations assumed openly their political goals and became political parties. Given the refusal of the Portuguese government to participate in any kind of dialogue, the only way out was armed conflict. The revolts began and became structured in organisations which grew in strength and in their capacity to make demands.
It was never possible to unite the élites who encouraged these movements. Age-old differences separated the urban élites from the rest of the rural aristocrats, with the arrogance of the former, in their belief that they were more advanced, clashing with the mistrust and resentment of the latter toward the privileged class who lived alongside the colonisers. Without doubt, this is one of the reasons for the split between the parties who were leading the battle for freedom, which lost impetus because of this division. The result was civil war, which broke out after Independence in November 1975. However, we cannot only blame differences between élites for this war, which is still going on. There were many other factors that aggravated the situation and that, taking advantage of these divisions, were able to reach to the heart of Angolan society and increased the fractures. One of them was ideological and grew from the century's great struggle between the socialist and capitalist systems, which culminated in the so-called Cold War. Angola suffered the interference of the powers fighting each other, an interference accentuated by the obvious greed of these powers for the

mineral wealth of the country. A second factor was that Angola was not a solidly unified Nation, the creation of which had been the aim of many intellectuals. Regional and ethnic differences coexisted with a unifying dominant culture which was in some ways artificial because of being too centralised in or from the capital. The leadership of some political factions took advantage of these differences in an attempt to reinforce their specific project, though with little success up till now. Together with these sociological, historical and political factors, there were also personal factors in the shape of the ambitions and resentments of some leaders who were incapable of recognising the superiority of anyone else. This brief summary of the causes and conditions of the conflict is enough to show that concentrated in one country alone are all the reasons for the outbreak of any of the civil wars that the world has seen in the 20th century -with the exception of religion. Fortunately, despite the existing differences between religions and churches, and even though the Catholic religion alone was recognised by the Portuguese metropolis and there were severe restrictions on any kind of protestant initiative, there were no rivalries or serious resentments between the different confessions. Contrary to what has happened in many other parts of the world, it cannot be said that the religious factor has caused divisions, or social fracture in Angola, beyond the usual differences between believers and non-believers, converts and those who are faithful to more traditional beliefs, Catholics and Protestants, and between all of these and the animists. From all that we have said up to now, we can draw a first conclusion: over the past centuries, a particular process of contact between European powers and local cultures and ruling bodies has been the cause of the growth of a concept of Nation. This is now a project which is at an advanced stage of evolution and has successfully resisted the centrifugal forces that might have thwarted it. Despite wars and other on-going conflicts, such as a civil war lasting more than twenty years and more violent than anything that has ever been seen in Africa, the Angolan people's wish is to stay together, in the belief that they will be able to build a society with a future in spite of all the rivalries, differences and resentments. Should we be surprised? I am, every day.

When I see children abandoned in the streets, hundreds of cripples wandering about begging in the middle of the chaotic traffic, ruined cities and burnt villages, families divided not only geographically but also psychologically and culturally, an economy which survives in a permanent and multifaceted imbalance, people who are too rich in comparison with the misery that so many others suffer, a corruption so generalised that it now has no sense and is just a way to survive, in the midst of all this, I ask myself: "Does this Country still exist?". Contrary to the predictions of those that study us and look on at us from outside, every new day brings more evidence that this Nation, surprisingly enough, is becoming consolidated. Perhaps, in the future, analysts will have an explanation. Is it possible that, despite the horror, the dialectics of war help to unite populations? I do not know, and I do not dare to formulate such a conclusion. But facts are facts. The 20th century saw the birth of a Project that, vicissitude by vicissitude, has been growing slowly and today can be called a Nation, in which the different elements may still be contradictory, sometimes violently so, but they do not break up or dissolve. There are some privileged moments when hearts can be heard beating as one, despite diverging interests and ideas, when a nation as a whole faces situations imbued with a huge collective symbolism. If this is not a sign of a collective will and emotion that constitute what we call national identity, then I really do not know what we are talking about. From a global point of view, what is valid for Angola is valid for Africa. The 20th century was that of colonisation and decolonisation, which led in most cases to modern identities that were the first steps in the creation of Nations from States. It is a process which is still in many different stages, more advanced in some countries and more fragile in others, probably the majority. In general, colonisation created borders that are artificial and extremely precarious since they do not correspond at all to the reality of the territory. In the act of constitution of the Organization of African Unity it was decided that these borders were to be respected by all. If one exception were to be allowed, with imposed divisions and annexations, a domino effect would probably be caused and there would be real chaos in Africa. Few States would remain unharmed.

This is why the question of the formation of nationalities is vital and must be studied without dogmatism and in depth. We have recent examples in a continent with apparently much more firmly established social and political structures. In Europe, the political map has changed dramatically in the last decade, a change which in itself would not be dramatic if it were not for the fact that it was brought about through massacres and huge sacrifices for the peoples of that continent. Africa, a continent that has been constantly devoured by vultures that come from other places to fly in her skies, has suffered so much and we must prevent any further hecatombs. One way of avoiding the disasters that are being foretold is to create balanced Nations and States, without the enormous social differences that seem to be hovering on the horizon. This can be done either separately or in large regional groups, taking into account what others have already done and the needs of each specific society. We will have to recognise that the economic viability of some African countries, especially those that are landlocked, is limited. Therefore it is vital they join others in regional groups, in the same way that the most important countries of Europe did, to build wider markets to make feasible what are known as economies of scale.

These are some of the lines along which we should work to reach a balanced solution for the century in Africa. I have left for the end what I think is the most important factor to be taken into account, without which nothing of what I have said up to now would have much sense. It is easy to say, even if putting it into practice has been impossible: it must be the African people who decide their destiny, because this is the first objective of any battle towards freedom.

Up until today, Africa has been an ungoverned toy, adrift on the stormy seas of competing foreign interests. Its own political, economic and social organisation was dictated from outside. First, it was colonisation that, "preaching Faith and Civilization", affirmed that it knew what was best for the peoples it dominated, as if the colonisers had ever asked themselves this. They imposed their model with the obligation to imitate the European states, or simply to copy the gestures, postures and movements of the white coloniser. The results were not at all satisfactory. The Africans did not know how to copy faithfully what the white man thought and did, or they simply did not wish to do it because it meant distancing themselves irremediably from their own identity. The results of attempting to create “black people with white souls” were superficial and only successful in a few cases. In fact, they disintegrated when sufficient conditions for rejection coincided. Each case of colonialism had different results, but in general they were only able to create élites that were isolated from the population, depersonalised and living with what was called the “complex of the colonised”. However, contrary to what was thought, this “complex” was not constructive, as it did not develop in the Africans a mentality that was similar to that of the coloniser but submissive. In those cases where the policy of assimilation was developed, the colonised people, while fearing the white man and admiring his capacity for mastering unknown technologies, developed hidden resentments because he knew he could never be considered his equal. He was only useful as an instrument for the domination of other autochthonous peoples that were further away from the colonial centres.

After independence, the fact is that either due to the changes experienced by the élites, affected by the complexes created by colonisation, or to factors related to the Cold War, some countries copied capitalist and others socialist models. Nevertheless, because these models were imposed from without and were applied without much thought, they were pale copies that would eventually fail. Today, with the victory of the capitalist and liberal model, we are experiencing the injection of massive doses of that miraculous elixir called “market economy”, universal and sacred panacea for all the ills that African societies suffer. Because a panacea cannot be applied in isolation, a second one has been imposed: parliamentary democracy. Since these two scientific discoveries have the backing of those competent and victorious agents, NATO, the IMF and the World Bank, Africa will successfully fly to the stars, once the turbulence of this turn of the century has been overcome. At least, this is what the owners of the world, with not a hint of a smile, are promising us... and there are some who believe them.

I believe it is time to stop and think. This was my intention a long time ago when I began to realise what the people who really have the power in the world expected from us. Africa must get together, as some other societies still do, under one or many wide-spreading trees, with the charitable spirits of our ancestors among the leaves, and talk about the future. We have to learn again the virtue of conversing calmly, pondering each case, with no hurry, because time is our own invention that we can change as we wish. We must talk and talk until we reach a consensus. This is how things were done in olden times and should still be done now when there are important matters to be discussed. We should not be afraid of being told that we are retrogrades, or lovers of traditions that have been outmoded by the frenzy of machines, or nostalgic for customs trampled on by scientific progress. They may use other such kind phrases, when in fact all they want to say is that we are backward.
Africa must think and talk. What about? About the future, naturally. We have to know what kind of society we want to live in. Are the satisfied and happy northern societies the model we must follow? Do we want to live like them? Do we want to give up some of our values, which are daily being crushed by our apathetic leaders who follow the dictates of the Masters of the World in order to impose the rational principles of social structure discovered in the West? Or perhaps we would like to invent models of society nearer to our own cultural origins, to our social norms and values, which have amazingly been able to resist the constant attempts to colonise our spirit?
Which form of economic and political organisation is the most appropriate for us? Is it the highly-praised parliamentary democracy, where citizens vote every four years for people whom nobody knows and who, during that period, do what they think they have to do in the name of those who voted for them? Using a method that means that some win and others lose? Or would it perhaps be worthwhile to try to reconcile this with the African principle of consensus, to the detriment of the exclusion of a minority, which is inevitably implicit in any election? These are complex questions which cannot be answered lightly. Perhaps it would also make sense to discuss the model of a liberal economy. Is it advisable to leave

to blind market forces the responsibility of establishing the relative value of things? Is a tortoise really worth the same as three kilos of corn? Can the ineffable IMF really determine these matters and many others from such a long way away? Will we have the courage, the imagination, the madness, give it whatever name you wish, to try to invent something new under the tree?

This is my challenge and my hope. That African people are daring enough to say stop, wait, it's our turn to decide. We accept your wonderful discoveries; we will adopt them as our own, from the bicycle to the computer. We also want societies ruled by the intransigent defence of the right of people to choose, to give opinions and to express themselves with total freedom, by means of institutions that guarantee this freedom and firmly prevent any form of oppression. These institutions must be our own institutions, which we can control and understand, governed by principles that we feel deep within us because they are rooted in our culture. Our wish is to create peace-loving societies with equal opportunities for everyone, not only for the privileged élites, by applying methods that we are able to carry out successfully, without violating the ethics which have been at the base of our society for the past thousand years.

This century will be African, if we are able to impose our own decisions on the Western centres of domination, which are deaf and blind, dazzled by their own power. If we have the courage to do this, we will be helping the rest of the world to find more human ways of developing. We will be helping towards self-comprehension even those parts of Humanity who convinced themselves of the irreversibility of their own progress and of the eternity of their economic, cultural and military power. Essentially, Africa will again be disseminating civilization, as it did in the beginning, when African people left to populate the rest of the earth.

Is it a dream, utopia, madness? Perhaps. I am aware that the great majority of people are not ready to hear such heresies. But how monotonous life would be without madness... And no Faith can survive without a heresy or two.

Tiérno Monénembo

Africa: like a ufo that never takes off

"Africa is a question mark". It was Sékou Touré who said this speaking as he did, tersely and sharply, but nevertheless expressing the obvious: Africa is disconcerting, Africa is disturbing, Africa is exasperating and even the Africans themselves are exasperating. It is believed to be a continent but it is only an abyss, an astral space of traps and barriers where problems proliferate and intertwine like lichens. It is the soft belly, the sick heart of the world. So awfully soft, so awfully sick, that nobody goes to its bedside any more! The "bitter, red lands" sung about by David Diop are at their limit. They now only wait for extreme unction, and the fact that to say so I must quote the cause of all my unhappiness –the man to whom I owe the ruin of my country and my thirty-five years in exile– best expresses the extent of my distress.
However, honesty obliges me to say that these are not the words of Sékou Touré the tyrant, the sinister vulture whose spirit still soars over the bones of the Boiro camp. They are of Sékou Touré the hero, the father of Guinean independence, one of the pioneers of African renaissance, which, let's face it, increases rather than lessens the drama. I told you, we are in the worst of countries, the world of the impossible where each glimmer of hope immediately generates the laws of its own death, leaving the horizon behind it darker and more distant than before. The glimmer of hope had a name at that time: Nkrumah, Lumumba, Cabral! Sékou Touré, no less! And a place: the rostrum of the United Nations. It was from this balcony of modern times that these words were spoken. It must have been 1959 or 1960 at the latest; in any case not far in time from the birth of the Federation of Mali, from the death of Lumumba and from the Sharpeville massacre. The dashing Guinean leader had already been in power for two years. Little time to build a cathedral, but enough to learn something of the affairs of the world and to rub shoulders with its most beautiful icons. It must have been during his second or third visit to New York. He had already come across that young, charismatic senator from Massachusetts launched on his path to the White House, who had himself called JFK and often had tea with Haïle Selassie and Nasser, Tito or Chou En-Lai.

Previously confined to the kitchens, the blacks were beginning to assault and occupy the front rows and the palaces. Yes, after centuries of chaos and troubles, of promises and dashed hopes, Africa was rising, this time for good, we thought. Magnificently thumbing her nose at Hegel and Renan, at Gobineau and the Chinese mandarins, she threw into the fire her sad reputation as an empty continent, as a kingdom of darkness "made to serve the great things desired and conceived by the white man". A new chrysalis was coming forth from her entrails, smashing into fragments her old cocoon of prejudice and hate, of curse and greed. And suddenly the stars lit up new gods finally made man and black-skinned, who roared like thunder and lightning and spat their furious, multimillenary desire for grandeur and freedom on the wrinkled skin of the west. And these were our gods, and the sparkling signs of this new aurora reflected not only independence, but also the frenzy with which we were abandoning infancy. For it was to the birth of a double spring that the times brought us: that of a new Africa and that of the generation (my generation) that was to personify it.

Today, now that time has played its part, that the dreams have dissipated, that those who we thought were angels have shown their true faces of grave-diggers and torturers, what is left of it all? An aftertaste of bile, a phenomenal hangover, an irrepressible feeling of rage and impotence. After so many centuries, so close to the goal! How in God's name is it possible?

But at the beginning of the 60s, everything favoured revival in Africa. Never had the times been so propitious! History, resentful and mean since the irruption of the Portuguese ships along its coast in the mid-15th century, suddenly seemed more enjoyable, more engaging. Thrown out of India and Pakistan, bogged down in the rice fields of Indochina and the sands of Kabylie, the colonial powers had lost much of their prestige and their strength. The white masters were no longer invincible. The future was becoming clearly possible, especially because completely fresh news was coming from Moscow and Prague. From that side of the world –European too, strangely enough– men were preaching the equality of races, the emancipation of colonies and friendship among peoples.

At last we were going to deal with our own affairs and talk on an equal footing with other civilisations, gather in the stadiums and congress halls with our heads held high, without seeing that suspicious, condescending expression which others usually wore when with us. It is true that this independence that had been so widely acclaimed had not changed very much. We were still suffering from leprosy and malaria. We were dying of hunger. Schooling was a luxury and health infrastructures were cruelly lacking. We still travelled on foot or on a donkey, entertained ourselves by the light of the stars and drank filthy water, but that didn't matter. The essential thing was there: the freedom to come and go, to get drunk and defecate without having to report to the whites. The rest would come much later. With the prison doors brought down, all we had to do was to let ourselves be carried along on the fresh breeze of freedom and allow new generations to grow; development would come automatically, as on our dry plains the ferns appear from nothing after the first rains.
Africa had everything for herself: nature, sea, mineral resources and ingenuousness. Little else was needed to propel her towards the lights of modernity. The statistics showed it and all the specialists agreed: the East was too metaphysical, Asia was overpopulated and Latin America, it must be said, was excessively involved in the irreversible reign of the mafias and oligarchies to attempt progress. But Africa...! Excessively archaic but receptive to evolution since she was devoid of all dogmatic heritage, the black continent resembled a piece of dough just waiting to be moulded by those experimenting in progress and development. "A little technology here, a lot of capital there and that's it", as they would say in the West. "You have understood nothing –they retorted on the other side of the Berlin wall– a little electricity here, a lot of Soviets there...". However, as they were saying this, all these great men had their eyes on the year 2000, with the superstition round numbers have always inspired. Men only talked about being on course for the year 2000, the horizon of 2000, being prepared for the year 2000, the dawn of the third millennium... One would think that on that date, between midnight and five minutes past midnight the whole world would be turned upside down. And where was Africa in all this? She watched events with the demure look

of our young girls listening to the elders discussing their own weddings, which obviously did not concern them, being as silly as they were. In any case, it didn't matter. Independence was there; the rest would come by itself. There was no need to sow to see the ferns grow. It was sufficient to stand on one's doorstep and watch the first rains fall...

Now that I think about it, it is this spirit that has led us to the dead end in which we are today. It is to our multimillenary culture of passiveness and fatalism that we owe these forty years of chaos and hate, of failure and ineptitude, of poverty and despotism. In fact, we suffer from everything: the anger of the elders, the thunderbolts of the gods, and in the same order of things, colonisation and independence, tyranny and democracy, progress and development. Everything here is catastrophic, even happiness.

There is nothing fortuitous about this catastrophe; it is not the result of the unclear laws and dictates of chance. It is part of an ancient, precise order: traditional culture. Land of the gods and dwelling of the Elders, Africa, more than any other world, honours and sanctifies the past. The world has been made (and well made) once and for all. Any attempt to revise or improve it would lead to decadence, sin, blasphemy. There is no need to rack one's brains. Our ancestors have thought of everything; the path has been marked. All that is needed in order to advance is to learn their spells and their proverbs. To disobey our ancestors is to upset the balance of the world. And that is all: a subtle game of balance, that is tradition. A balance between man and nature; between nature and the gods; between earth and the cosmos; between the individual and the group; between clans and empire; between needs and resources...

Tradition is the constant search for harmony. But modernity is quite the opposite; it is a violent, disorganised process that progresses blow by blow, by upheavals, by cataclysms. Tradition speculates, modernity decides. Modernity schemes, tradition contemplates.

These are two antagonistic, irreconcilable worlds. These are the two extremes of contemporary Africa. It is Scylla and Charybdis, if the dilemma still has any sense in a continent that is already lost. The first world is immutable and adheres, so that it is impossible to break away from it. The second world is noxious and magnetic, impossible to escape from. A synthesis would have been desirable, but how, when like all Africans today, the continent is a monster with two heads? For it is not according to the laws of physics that things happen: it is in our being, in our very conscience where these two worlds move apart and exclude each other. The world of our ancestors is comfortable, cosy, reassuring, even though we do not fully know its mysteries and we have little mastery of its spells and rites. The white man's world is fascinating, though it sickens us with its alluring flashiness and superficiality. To tell the truth, deep down we have always disdained it slightly; yes, it is through wanting to ignore it that Africa has suffered, and continues to suffer, Europe. Africa has long believed that the irruption of the European navigators along her coasts was not only fortuitous, but that it would necessarily be provisional. As for the white man, with his feverish agitation and his insistence on discovery and invention, Africa has always considered him puerile and reckless. She watches him calmly while he juggles with danger, waiting for him to fall flat on his face and to be able to say didactically and triumphantly, "You see! I told you so over and over again, you little rascal!" The problem is that the rascal never falls, quite the contrary; all his exploits become new eras of civilisation, each of his mad feats a new order in the world. The idea has backfired! If La Fontaine were still living he would undoubtedly write us a fable using this strange story where for once it is the imbecile who triumphs and the wise man who loses out. But this has been going on for nearly five centuries! This is no longer a game, if it ever were one! The troublemaker has won right down the line, and each of these victories has confirmed his idea that conquering, dominating and defeating are his most natural right. Master of science and art, organiser of life on earth and of the laws that govern space, he accumulates victories and trophies without faltering, without it affecting him in any way. His machines forge through space, his values shape societies, his ideas nourish spirits. He truly has something to boast about. We can be jealous or feel resentment, but cannot fail to admire him. My frustrations from being under-developed do not prevent me from admiring Copernicus and Michelangelo, Claude Bernard and Einstein; the sewing machine and the laser beam.

This is also Christian Europe, the civilisation that has ruthlessly devastated all the civilisations of the world; the army that has defeated all the armies of the world; the way of thinking that has eclipsed all other ways of thinking in the world. And this most lucid of tributes should not be interpreted as the result of a black man's complex. We are in the year 2004. The political leanings of Hegel and Gobineau, Renan and Lévy-Bruhl, Goebbels and Hitler and of others of their kind are long behind us, as are Caesar and Senghor with their legitimate, but inflamed, lyricism of precentors of negritude. Today it is generally admitted that the evolution of society owes nothing to the exellences of race. Now we can set aside prejudices of colour and go calmly into societies to study the way they work, I was going to say their physiology. And what do we see? That Europe was not always the first, that before it other civilisations had studied territories and matter, mathematics and philosophy. So why Europe and not Egypt or Mesopotamia, India or the empire of Monomotapa, China or the Aztec empire? Why have the Arabs, who gave us Abou Nouwas and Omar Khayam, the compass and astronomy, the scalpel and algebra, degenerated to give way completely to the descendents of their enemies, the crusaders? For a very simple reason, which is that Europe, by means of its damned renaissance, dared to do what no other civilisation had dared to do before: break with its past. This continent has been the first to put its culture in a museum. I visit the legacies of ancestors while I pay my respects to the dead. My culture is no longer what I inherit; it is what I reinvent each day. I am no longer the depositary of a culture, I am the generator of culture. It is here too where man for the first time dared to reform the word of the good God; notice that modernity is above all a story of protestants. Yes, what a cheek! This is undoubtedly what made Poincaré say, “The school of invention is the school of disrespect”.

Since then, all emerging civilisations have had to go through the same experience, breaking with their past. Without the deep structural and mental changes of the Meiji era, Japan would not have known nylon or the transistor, the generators of its development. Is it not symptomatic that on coming to power, Mao's first words were “It is necessary to demolish the house of Confucius?" As for Russia, they started by singing *The Internationale* ("we'll change henceforth the old tradition") before giving birth to Yuri Gagarin.

And Africa's misfortune arises from this: she does not know how to break with the past. Here, all change is experienced as betrayal. The past sticks to our skin like a monstrous appendix, like an incurable tumour. The result is this pitiful comedy: in the morning we play at being elders and at midday, when the violent light of reality begins to blind us, we play at being the white man. We have never learnt to play at being ourselves. We continue to be persuaded (in our subconscious at least) that our world cannot be disturbed and that, like the sun or the good God, it will remain unharmed by all the uproar down there. Look how nostalgically we have experienced our independences! Everything took place as though, after the departure of the white man, life would be as it was before colonisation; our encounter with the West would be no more than a brief parenthesis. Look at the State of sorcerers and marabous that Sékou Touré left to Guinea! Look at the ghost of Moslem integrism that the FLN created in Algeria!

True, colonisation neither defines us nor creates us. Only, whether we like it or not, it came at a crucial moment in our history. To paraphrase Sheik Hamidou Kane, we are no longer a different Africa facing a different West. Henceforth the West is part of us from head to toe, like the unforgettable smell of a lover, like the pains of cancer or rabies. By the most pernicious of paradoxes, the Europe that is at the root of all our misfortunes has become, whether we like it or not, our last resort. It will be of no help to us to shelter eternally under the boubou of the elders; we must very quickly create our own modernity. Now, this is impossible without studying in the school of the West, without understanding the way of thinking that has allowed it to deploy such gigantic energy. It is so true, and the Japanese and Chinese experiences are good examples, that it is impossible to free oneself from the West without a minimum of westernisation. To be modern, it will not be sufficient to drive a Mercedes and talk on a cell phone; we will have to assimilate the ideas and methods that have produced them. We are far from achieving this. None of our politicians, none of our intellectuals have yet learnt the lesson of our collision with Europe. And this is the cause of our disarray, our stagnation.

We are overwhelmed by debts and epidemics. Aids decimates us, hunger makes us blind and deaf. With almost 12% of the population of the world, we produce hardly 2% of its wealth.

Does this mean that Africa is dying, as some grave-diggers turned necrologists say, licking their chops? Of course not. Africa is tough and has lived through harder times than this. I sometimes think that history is a boxing match and those who know how to take the punches are those who end up winning.

Africa is sick, I agree, but she is a patient who has reason to hope. She has 55% of the world reserves of raw materials. She is young (nearly 50% of her population is under fifteen) and like all youngsters, she has boundless enthusiasm. And thanks to her philosophy, Africa has always been a privileged accomplice of life. In fact, this is where there is still pleasure and laughter. The young lad who polishes shoes in Ouagadougou or Niamey never thinks of death. His whole being is concentrated on those two or three euros he must earn every day to feed his brothers and sisters and look after his mother's cough. And he knows he will get those two or three euros whatever stumbling blocks have to be overcome or whatever storms have to be weathered.

Africa is certainly in chaos, but a rich chaos, a fruitful chaos (similar to that of the Middle Ages in Europe). Something will come out of it, something new, something strong.

What does it matter whether it is tomorrow or in five thousand years' time?

Véronique Tadjo

The Ivory Coast and the new millennium

>I Just before 24th December 1999

Some time ago in Abidjan, youngsters played a very dangerous game which consisted of catching onto a moving bus, climbing on the roof and doing handstands. They called this game *Le bôro d'enjaillement*, a name that they had invented themselves and which came from the language of the streets, always in full evolution. *Bôro* means "bag" in Malinke and *enjaillement* is a deformation of the French word *joie*, which means "pleasure". Therefore, the literal translation is 'bag of pleasure". The pleasure comes from the risk, the bag is doubtless the body we carry, the mass of our flesh. This activity was carried out particularly in the town of Yopougon, on the outskirts of Abidjan, on a route used regularly by private buses. The game had its winners, stars with the names of "Xena", "One arm", "The fly", "The devil", who left their *graffiti* on the walls of the bus. According to the precise rules of the game, the semi-finals could only be held on Wednesdays and the finals on Fridays. Individuals and school institutions took part after class, between half past twelve and half past two or between half-past six and eight o'clock. In the town, the inhabitants were amazed, hypnotised by the acrobatics of the youngsters on the bus roofs. Sometimes spectators gathered along the route to applaud.
It took the death of a boy and several accidents to cause an exceptional mobilisation to stop this suicidal game that was threatening to spread to other districts of the city. Parents of pupils, heads of schools, municipal councillors, forces of order and agents from the bus company met to decide on a strategy. Some thought that the movement could have started in some private bus companies that use youngsters to tie down the passengers' luggage on top of the vehicles. These are youngsters who are normally unemployed or school drop-outs who do this to earn a little money. The driver of the vehicle often does not wait for the youngster to finish tying down the luggage before starting off. For others it was rather the influence of television. In fact at this time, one of the episodes of an American series that was being broadcast by the Ivory Coast television showed some adolescents who climbed onto the roofs of

carriages to show off. Whatever it was, this suicidal period of the youth of the Ivory Coast shook society.
And here once again, the people of the Ivory Coast seem to be suffering this suicidal madness, but this time it's not the young who are playing with fire, but the whole of our national élite. No-one knows what's happening any more. The tone has hardened, people are becoming radical and adopting rigid attitudes. Faces are contracted, anxious, muscles are tense, moods sharp, ready to attack. Daily life no longer flows calmly, everyone has to take up a position, declare, show allegiances. The country is cracking, is splitting into two parts; on the one side the South, and on the other the North. The forthcoming presidential elections are aggravating the tensions and it is only necessary to say the name Alassane Ouattara for a bitter debate to start. Everyone thinks they are in possession of the truth concerning the authenticity of the nationality of this former Prime Minister of the Ivory Coast.

Is he or isn't he one hundred per cent from the Ivory Coast?

Could his nationality certificate be false?

Does he or does he not have the right to aspire to being the maximum authority?

According to the last official statement, he is not entitled to be a candidate in the presidential elections, but there is no point in reasoning in favour of one side or the other; it is a question of faith. One believes or one does not believe in the full citizenship of Alassane Ouattara. The discussion goes round in circles, tempers fly. How could the people of the Ivory Coast have come to this?
Some years before all of this, before the death of Houphouët Boigny, such a discussion would not have taken place, because the word "Ivoriness" did not exist. People were not concerned with knowing whether your parents or your parents' parents were a hundred per cent from the Ivory Coast. The Ivory Coast had the reputation of being a welcoming land and a large number of foreigners lived there. After

independence, when the Ivory Coast economy needed labour, Houphouët Boigny declared, "Let the foreigners come, it is God who sends them." As in many African countries, the population of the Ivory Coast was formed by the successive migrations of peoples who lived in the fringe regions. The frontiers were not the same as today because they were established more for linguistic, cultural or religious reasons. If we consider the example of the *baoulé* people, from which President Konan Bédié comes, one of the most popular legends of oral tradition is that of Abla Pokou, the queen who had to escape from Koumassi in Ghana, to flee from a war of succession in the Ashanti kingdom. With her faithful people, she crossed the whole of Ghana and came to the frontier of what is now the Ivory Coast. Impeded by the great river Comoé, she was obliged to sacrifice her son to save her people. When she threw the little boy into the water, it opened to allow her faithful people to pass, and these were able to settle and found the *baoulé* Kingdom, the name of which means "the child is dead".

The word "Ivoriness" is a vague concept that attempts to define the identity and values of the people of the Ivory Coast. But it is a concept which, when used to exclude, can be very dangerous. In its name we fight others for what they are and not for what they have done, and now the conflicts are multiplying. The demonstrations in the streets generate repressive measures. Twelve members of the RDR, the party of Alasane Ouattara have been arrested. A death has occurred during a territorial dispute in the South West, and several hundred *burkinabé* people have been chased from the region.

There is a great fear of exclusion. The people who live in the "Great North" are mainly Muslim and *malinké*. They share the *dioula* language with the inhabitants of Burkinabe and Mali. Even the surroundings are different in the north of the Ivory Coast, the scenery is more Sahelian than in the south of the country, everything is green and lush. If things continue this way, the people in the north are going to feel alienated, and what makes the situation even more dangerous is that there is an economic imbalance between the north and the south, where income is

concentrated, with Abidjan using up a large part of the resources.
Are we not simply facing a conflict of interests?
The Akan group under the regime of Houphouët Boigny stayed in power for over fourty years. Konan Bédié belongs to the same group. Houphoët Boigny, a charismatic leader, managed to maintain a certain ethnic balance that gave the impression of a stable, moderate country; however, he left us a terrible legacy symbolised by the Yamoussokro Basilica, which he built at great expense in his native "village", now the political capital of the Ivory Coast. He taught us that "charity begins at home". Before dreaming of the good of one's country, one must think first of satisfying one's own needs, those of one's family, one's clan, one's ethnic group, one's region. What is happening today in Daoukro, the "village" of Konan Bédié, is of the same order. If politics had not been the best way to get rich and distribute money, the problem would not have been stated in ethnic terms, but the way things are, the people of the North are claiming what they consider belongs to them and do not want to wait any longer, and this in a country that is not economically sound. Following two financial scandals involving the Ministry of Public Health and the Price Stabilisation Bank, for the time being, the IMF has refused to release funds for the Ivory Coast, which it considers to be undermined by corruption. The educational system is in crisis, shaken by regular strikes; unemployment casts many people onto the street, who soon become easy prey to all kinds of political manipulation.
Before the crisis of the Great North, it was the *bétés* in the south-west who were rejected by the Government. Laurent Gbagbo, the leader of the Ivory Coast Popular Front had long been the government's pet aversion until the arrival of Alassane Ouattara on the political scene. Now Laurent Gbagbo waits to play his cards, and his alliance with one side or the other might be decisive for the future of the country.
The conditions are gradually coming together for open ethnic conflict.
In a country where there has been peaceful co-existence for several generations, how has it been possible to invent the concepts of frontier and rupture, create a vacuum around an ethnic group and claim violently that the others

are foreigners that are not entitled to benefit from all their rights?

We are bound to go deeper into the question of what violence really is in contemporary Africa. In the case of the Rwandan massacre, or in the conflicts in Sudan, Somalia, Angola, Liberia and Sierra Leone, without forgetting the two Congos, it is necessary to get to the root of the problem, to dissect the violence of power and the political manipulations that have been propagated throughout society. Under the disguise of democracy, many regimes create a society in which ethnic feelings are exacerbated. This has undoubtedly been the case of Rwanda, which for many years had the reputation of being a country where a tolerant population was the best guarantee of stability. However, before the genocide there had already been episodes of political-ethnic violence which had caused a significant number of deaths and the exodus of thousands of Rwandan people.

The analysts have considered that the existence of a young population –drop-outs from school or youngsters who had never ever been to school, who were therefore often on the fringe– is a factor that favoured genocide. Having broken free from the family unit but still bearing the weight of a rural background, it was mainly this group that was at the base of the violence, as has usually been the case throughout Africa. It is these who have formed the bulk of the members of the *interhamwe* and the militias that have sown terror throughout the country. The genocide in Rwanda was not caused, as we have been led to believe, by a homicidal madness that suddenly descended on the country, but by the obstinate refusal of a part of the political class to face the risk of opening up and sharing power.

But the Rwandan tragedy also illustrates another problem, that of the international management of a crisis which, in addition to being of an unprecedented dimension, forms part of a world order that has lost its sense of political and ethnic direction. The proliferation of arms in African markets in areas of conflict jeopardises the stability of the continent. There is no small war; arms circulate and generate an atmosphere of tension for neighbouring countries, and when peace returns after the suffering, national reconciliation is difficult. We sometimes witness, as in the case of Rwanda, a situation of underlying conflict where peace is imposed more by force than by national consensus.

>II 24th December 1999

It is Christmas Eve. I am decorating the tree with my children. It is raining outside. It is cold. The telephone rings. A friend tells me there has just been a *coup d'etat* in the Ivory Coast. A *coup d'etat*! My head spins. I think of my father, relatives, friends, of how worried they must be. I immediately call my father in Abidjan. Thank God the telephone lines have not been cut. I hear the ringing in the emptiness and finally my father's voice as clear as if he were by my side. He confirms the news he heard on Radio France Internationale, as the national radio signal has been muted, just like the television, which is not broadcasting any programmes at all. The whole world is waiting to hear fresh news; the country is waiting to discover its fate. The person behind the coup, General Guéï, is known to the people of the Ivory Coast as a member of the former government, which replaced him.

What is he going to do with his power? Keep it or prepare elections? I am told that shots have been heard in the city; it seems that the soldiers are shooting into the air.

Hypnotised by the conflict between Henri Konan Bédié and Alassane Ouattara, we have not been able to see where the other danger lay, or maybe we haven't wanted to see it. We have seen political acrobatics, concentrated all our efforts on a futile debate that hid much broader questions. What will happen now? The Ivory Coast has rejoined the category of banana republic; a coup d'etat and the possibility of an attempted counter coup are always feasible.

We hear the news on the BBC. The overthrown President, Henri Konan Bédié, declares that the coup is grotesque and calls the population to hold firm by whatever means possible. He says that he is speaking from his office, but the commentator thinks that he is probably in the residence of the French ambassador. Even though the French troops, the BIMA, are stationed in Abidjan, there is no sign of an attempt to support the former regime. The journalist continues with the information that one of the first actions of General Guéï has been to free all political prisoners. I know the coming hours will be decisive. Chaos must not be allowed to reign in the streets as has happened in so many African countries when there has been a violent change of leadership. Groups start looting and sowing fear, taking advantage of the confusion caused by the fall of the former leaders. I think of my father, alone at home. How is he going to protect himself? He cannot go out. He must not go out into the street. I dream of my friends, of their concern.

The country is in turmoil at night. Insomnia, imagining what the future holds. The idea of a new government is taking shape. The people are called to their homes. Consultations, speculations, rumours everywhere. Some men and women are frightened, others are delighted and weigh up their opportunities, seeking in the past reasons to celebrate a change. Some people would like to flee, to leave the country under the cover of darkness. Others seek to return as soon as possible. Great decisions must be taken quickly, immediately; this is not the time for doubt. The coming hours will be decisive. Families break up, separate; friends betray each other. Alliances are formed, promises are made; it is time to make prognoses, strategies, projections.

The country will never be the same again. This earthquake has turned it upside down; I have the impression that my land is being snatched from me.

>III 25th December 1999

After a difficult night, I call my father once more. He is well but there has been looting in the city. A curfew has been declared. Apart from the political detainees, hundreds of common law prisoners have been freed; it seems that the military have simply opened the doors to the prisons. The government, the assembly and the constitution have been dissolved. General Guéï declares that democracy will continue. He will stay until the country recovers and new elections are held. I think of all the promises made by the military after coups in other African countries.

How many have had them? A Committee for Public Welfare is formed.
I call a friend. She tells me that the looting goes on; they no longer only attack department stores and shops, but also residences. The soldiers stop the cars, make the drivers get out and go off with the vehicles.
The largest supermarket in Abidjan has been rifled. The people stay at home, locking themselves in. The members of the government have been arrested, it seems that the fallen President is in the BIMA. General Guéï agrees to let him leave the country in peace; the French can help him leave. A French battalion will come to ensure the protection of the French citizens. Laurent Gbagbo is in Libreville, where he has accepted defeat in the negotiations regarding the conflict between Henri Konan Bédie and Alassane Ouattara.
I call another person. My friend tells me that some members of the Government are in the airport and they are not allowed to leave. The looting continues, buildings are burnt. Will the calm ever return? It seems more prisoners have been freed.
A period of prolonged anarchy would be disastrous.

>IV 26th December 1999
This is real exile. My country is shrinking before my eyes; will I recognise it when I return? How many things will have changed? And will I be recognised by those who have experienced these events? The Ivory Coast is going down the same road as so many other African countries. It was said to be a stable nation, an economic triumph. We will have to start again, rebuild an identity smashed by this act.
Somebody said, "The people of the Ivory Coast have preferred a *coup d'etat* to a poor democracy". I remember the course on African politics I had taken in SOAS, London, some years ago. One of my teachers had a theory on the coups in Africa. He considered that it might be a progressive factor in societies where the rules of the democratic game were not applied. The takeover of power by force became the only alternative for change.
Today, I want to believe it.

>V 27th December 1999

It seems that the Ivory Coast was heading towards an open ethnic conflict. Will this coup help to break through the existing impasse or plunge the country into even greater chaos? Is it the end of a power that has lasted over fourty years? Will this upheaval completely change the structure of society of the Ivory Coast, especially of its ruling class? Is it the dawn of a renewal or the beginning of a long night?
I get information on the Internet. All the main newspapers in the Ivory Coast have a website where it is possible to read complete articles. I consult them one by one and then print out those that interest me. The photographs, the official declarations, the positioning of one or the other, the names of the members of the former government who have been arrested, the reports, everything appears on the screen of my computer. Everything seems unreal. Is it my country they are talking about?
General Guéï talks to the political parties. He explains how he has come to the forefront of the coup d'etat. He talks about the bloodbath that has been avoided by the skin of our teeth, of the ethnic conflict that was brewing. The course of the country had to be corrected. Then he assures us that the presence of the generals, French nationals from the north, in the National Committee for Public Welfare does not mean that the military regime is close to Alassane Ouattara. He promises to organise elections when new laws have been drawn up and voted, without setting a date. In the Great North, it is all rejoicing; songs, dancing, cheering, applause, everything is festive. Since the announcement of the fall of Dédié's government, the streets have been full of celebrating crowds.

>VI 28th December 1999

Abidjan seems to have recovered its calm; activities have gone back to normal. People are going about their business, soldiers are seen less and less in the streets but the police and the gendarmes are still there. The banks receive their customers. However, in some districts the shops are still closed. Public transport is working once more; there are crowds at the bus-stops. The markets are open. A loincloth seller shouts into the

journalist's microphone: "We are happy Bédié's page has been turned. We look forward to the second republic". The Houphouët Boingy international airport, closed during the events, is now open again.
Is the Ivory Coast peaceful once more?

>VII The new millennium

On the eve of the year 2000, the Ivory Coast is still clearly representative of Africa: nervous, fragile, shaken by endless convulsions.
With the end of the old regimes, are we finally on the path to a state of less corruption and fewer economic disasters? Will we be able to break the cycle of civil wars and armed conflicts? Will popular pressure make all civil and military regimes accountable for their actions? The national conferences in Benin, the Congo, Niger, Zaire, Madagascar and other places show clearly a desire to see the establishment of a new political order, and the civil wars devastating the continent represent an attempt to redraw the frontiers inherited from colonisation, to renegotiate the limits of nations.
Africa must find her own way and define her future for herself, while the former colonial powers must increasingly relinquish their hold. Paradoxically, the incessant crises, the frequent descents into hell, will in the end give the African peoples control over their own destinies once more and oblige them to demand of their leaders greater integrity and social justice.

Víctor Omgbá

Africa, the hopeless continent

Quo Vadis, Africa? The age-old question from the days of the Roman Empire could very well be applied to African countries in the 21st century. Where is Africa going? Is there any hope left for the millions of men and women of this continent? René Dumont already made his prediction long ago: Africa's development had got off on the wrong foot. Fifty years later, the prophecy still holds true. And nothing seems capable of changing it. The continent is sinking while our politicians do nothing more than applaud. It is going through a situation of disillusionment, and a lack of political, economic and social commitment. There is no morning. The African morning is an illusion. It is not surprising that there are so many victims knocking at the doors of the western fortress, trying to get in whatever the cost.

Over and above this sad reality looms the shadow of a none too well handled past. The continent, as historian Joseph Ki Zerbo said, did not do its homework. It put the cart before the horse. Let us take a look at some examples.

To go about their own reconstruction, even in the midst of the euphoria sparked by the clarion call of independence, many African countries decided to educate their children by relying on the models they had inherited. Undoubtedly this was very laudable, but irredeemably wrong. They developed theoretical education systems with no consideration for the social needs of the time and no regard for their future worth. There was no culture of science, an aberration that resulted in the continent having to basically rely on the outside world.

This wretched situation was compounded by the need to defend borders that had been drawn up ambiguously by the West. The consequence was that African countries found themselves competing for antiquated arms left over from World War II. They spent, and they go on spending, enormous sums of money on military material that should have been earmarked for education and health, the keys to the development of any nation. Arms that some would never get to use or that others would use to kill each other, providing the whole world with the spectacle of a

genocide like the one we witnessed a few years ago in the area of the Great Lakes.
Africa is the continent that has been the most severely punished by HIV, with 25.4 million affected out of a total of 39.4 million worldwide. South Africa is suffering worst from the scourge of the virus, with 5.3 million victims. In countries like Zimbabwe life expectancy was fifty two years in 1990; now it has fallen to thirty four. In Swaziland, more than 30% of pregnant women carry the virus. To this disaster must be added the high price of drugs, making them unavailable to most people. Mention must also be made of the secular power of witch doctors, which is gaining in importance as it seeks to solve a catastrophic situation with cheap witchcraft. And so the fight against HIV runs into insurmountable obstacles.
Behind the social influences there are also geopolitical factors that stem largely from wars, political instability and corruption, conditions that conspire to cast a dark shadow over a continent besieged by internal conflicts. Yesterday it was the Great Lakes. Today it is the Ivory Coast that is trying hard to prove to the international community that everything is just a powder keg. It is all about wars that sprout on a social fabric turned gangrenous by major pandemics and which make any help impossible. It is difficult to push through programmes that effectively fight disease amidst bombs, tanks and antipersonnel mines.
Undoubtedly this is a continent that is categorised as totally lacking in importance for the rest of the world. In 1960, with African independence just around the corner, the continent represented 10% of worldwide commerce. Today, with 13% of the world's population, its participation in international commercial trade is barely 1.8%. Half this percentage is taken up by South Africa.
The responsibility rests firmly with the Africans themselves and their leaders who, sitting upon their petty thrones, help to impoverish their people by feathering their own nests, as well as those of their families and clans. In Africa, ethnicity and religion have become safe havens, where leaders boost their political dominance, surrounding themselves

with totally inexperienced and worthless technocrats: they disgracefully sanction the looting of people's wealth through capital flight, money lent contractually through the Paris Club, the World Bank and IMF loans. It is ignominious to see how heads of state scour European palaces with their begging bowls, soliciting money, knowing only too well where it will end up. There is nothing strange about the fact that we need up to 106 years to repay a colossal debt, estimated to be 1,500 billion francs, with Sub-Saharan Africa accounting for more than 1,000 billion.
We may draw the conclusion that, in the face of this acute crisis, Africa, the mother of humanity, has been left behind and it will require whole generations before it gets back on track and finds its place in the company of the continents that represent this planet, dominated by a globalisation that is strictly unilateral. *Quo Vadis*, Africa?

Yvonne Vera

A type of spider

In Africa there is a type of spider which turns to air, its life a mere gasp. It vanishes, from the inside out, its legs a fossil, an outline in the future. In Africa there is a type of spider which gathers all its kin before an earthquake, sending messages through the a r. Together the family gathers into a cubicle of timea bowl in a peeling rock, a basin where the earth has been eaten by rain; before an earthquake, befo-e the advance of an enemy, and war. Spider after spider piles into a mound, into a self-inflicted ruin, seeking another kind of escape. Then the top of this spider-mound is sealed with spit, thick and embroidered like lace, bright with sun rays, and rainbow arching like memories. A stillness gathers, before an earthquake, before war. There is a stillness such as has not been witnessed before, and a new climate in that trapped air. Turning and turning, again and again till something is free like a kindness. A spider falls like a pendulum stilled. This is not hibernation for a death: the bodies take flight, free as time. The body vanishes, f-om ins de out. The inside pouring like powdered dust, the legs a fossil. This is the end of creation, the beginning of war. Often, there is a cataclysmic innocence which knows nothing but death.

"... Spider legs", he insisted, after the war had ended. I heard of spider rituals from my uncle Sibaso in 1980, after the armed struggle which freed us from British rule. It was to me an astounding truth to hear, no, to witness, how my uncle ate spider legs throughout the war. He said this was because he knew where spiders went off to die. Was this not a great secret to know, he asked me. In the bush survival is a skill hewn fromthe harmonies of nature: nature is an elaboration of the disharmonies of war. My uncle Sibaso returned to Bulawayo with elaborate claims about the delicacy of our humanity –I only listened to him. He said we were a tenuous species, a continent which had succumbed to a violent wind. I listened to him with a shocked understanding. He said he hadharvested handfuls of spider-legs during the war. Who was I to contradict him –a mere girl who had never left the confines of Luveve township where I was born. He had an imagination that claimed supemacy ove- war, somehow. I knew I could harvest wisdom straight from his mouth.

He slept on the cracked floor of our verandah, polished a brilliant red every morning, with the stars falling straight into his mouth as he snored. How had he survived the war with such a glutinous snore. Yet he had lived to tell many illicit versions of the war even when it seemed unlikely he would be believed. The war had provided him a burden of memory. His future seemed always leaning toward an impeccable horizon. I adored his indifferent embrace of the stars. I envied his type of truth which sounded exactly like a well constructed lie.

Our country needed this kind of hero who had a balm for his own wounds, carried between lip and tongue, between thumb and forefinger, between the earth and the soles of his feet. He was in flight towards an immaculate truth and I followed him closely. Together we sat on garbage cans and watched the cars from Lobels, from Downings, from Haefelis. All of these were Bakeries located in the city centre. We watched the papaws fall off the trees at the beginning of the rainy season, and caterpillars curl into rings. A man who worked at Downings told us that they mixed the doug with goomboots, the same way we pounded our blankets when we washed them.

One day a van with a loudspeaker drove past and announced a new product for cleaning our teeth. My uncle Sibaso laughed till he fell asleep. I woke him to tell him that free toothpaste was being distributed door to door, by a lady in a wig. He said it was probably poisoned and we would die a slow death. It would take us about ten years to die. Our teeth would be whiter and firmer but our souls would be dead. After all our bodies had already died with the war. My uncle Sibaso kept the toothpaste in a secret place. The future remained ominous.

When I close my eyes to sleep, I have the sensation of drowning. I see a multitude of spider legs stretch into the void which leaps above me, that is the other strange fact about spiders, their ability to walk on water, while humans drown.

On the day of the cease-fire my uncle Sibaso left his unit and walked till he stood next to a railway station at Cement Siding. He rode from Cement Siding to Bulawayo on the goods train while resting on a single coach full of warm glittering coal. He removed his shirt and blended into the coals. He could feel the breeze and the juting edges of the coals on his back, the humid warmth. He watched the smoke form patterns above his head. He jumped off at Mpopoma Station before the train entered the Main Station in Bulawayo. Before the wheels ground to a stop he had fallen into the night; his dark skin protecting him against police whistles, sliding with curiosity and abandon into the music of bicycle pumps at Nandi Bazaar with its wide veranda and long wooden benches, along Bambazonke Road, where the men formed semi-circles and raised greased stems of Hercules bicycle pumps to their lips. Thin rubber stems inside the pumps, vacuum filled, rending high notes. I found him in that quaint music wrought from the stems of bicycle pumps. A type of music which pleaded for you to return to the hurt, to flee from joy. That one, Sibaso, he had a story to tell.

"I have seen a spider dancing with a wasp", he says. This type of spider hangs from asbestos ceilings in every township home. I am told that most politicians in Africa learnt their tricks from watching the motions of such spider. Dancing with a wasp.

Sibaso has beautiful fingers. I wonder how he fought the war with fingers which taper into such a firm an determined gentleness, his skin dark like honey, and always, a certain kind of joy clogging his eyes.

When he arrived from the bush, first he was employed in the Zimbabwe Republican Police. BSAP. That was during the struggle. Sibaso preferred the brown thick uniform of ZRP to the garments of war which the army wears. He wanted no reminders of camouflage though he had been offered a desk and a swivel chair, and had toured the officer's mess at Mbizo Barracks with its ornate but torn leather chairs, the alcool wafting past every dream, clear liquor suspended in tall cylinders which said Rhodesia. He saw a photo of himself in the bush holding an AK rifle, in an army magazine, and that concluded that. The caption called him an enemy of the people, a terrorist. He wondered how the picture had been taken without him noticing. If someone had pointed a camera at him they could equally have pointed a gun. He became immediately suspicious about his survival. He tore off the page and brought it home. He pasted it on his bed.

Sibaso became a policeman. High boots. Large brown belt on which he sat and carefully spread Nugget shoe polish on every weekend, let it dry, then polished till it gleamed. The same with his boots. He placed his hat on a hook very high off the ground so that no one could touch it. He liked being back in Luveve and being a policeman. He was the wrong height for a policeman but he was permitted to join because he had fought in the bush and deserved to be a policeman more than anyone else. Sibaso made a short and handsome policeman.

However, he was immensely disappointed that the country could no longer provide bicycles to well trained policeman, even those who had an exemplary army record, and instead made them walk undistinguished, to a crime scene. He would have liked to drive a jeep, for example, in which he had been thrown into as a youth. He wanted evidence of reversal. There were only a few jeeps left. Instead, my uncle Sibaso had to stand on the side of the road and wave down a lift from potential criminals. Being a policeman offered too many moments of humiliation and powerlessness. He started to detest it a little, amd to doubt the value of his return.

My uncle Sibaso says in Africa, there is a type of spider which changes coluor when mating. It devours its own partnernand rolls her into a fine paste. With this it courts his next partner. It offers her this round, perfectly prepared sacrifice in exchange for a brief but sweet liaison. This type of spider hangs between trees and can only be viewed in the light of a full moon. Such a spider possesses a valuable secret, the knowledge that love cannot be founded on mercy, but that mercy can be founded on love. It knows the true agony of ecstasy, that violence is part of the play of opposites, and that during war, there are two kinds of lovers: the one located in the past, and dead, the one in the future, living and more desirable.The past a repast, the future a talisman. This kind of truth also belongs to the fantasy of a continent in disarray.

Each evening when my uncle Sibaso was walking home he held a folded newspaper tightly in his armpit. He read about a policeman who had taken a bribe. My uncle decided to resign immediately from the ZRP, formerly known as BSAP. After he left, he read about another policeman who stole a watch from the distended arm of a dead politician who had been involved in a horrible accident along the Bulawayo-Victoria Falls roads. He had heat a donkey and his car swerved. Then he had hit a large truck from a tobacco company and that had crushed him to pieces. His gold watch lay gleaming on the side of the road where his arm lay. Sibaso felt glad to have followed his impulse to resign when he did. At least no one would ask him for an explanation concerning this widely reported police crime. Then another policeman was discovered wearing a woman's underwear after fainting during the nineteenth independence day celebrations, and Sibaso vowed that he would not read the newspaper again. He is currently considering joining the army, but does not want to be sent to the Democratic Republic of Congo where Zimbabwe is involved in the civilian war.

He is waiting.

Time is as necessary for remembering as for forgetting. Even the smallest embrace of pain needs a time larger than a pause, the greatest pause requires an eternity, the greatest hurt a lifetime. A lifetime is longer than eternity: an eternity can exist without human presence.
Since leaving ZRP my uncle has been gathering a certain kind of spider and pinning it down between the pages of his King James bible. This is a tall spider with long, long legs that are terryfingly thin, ready to disappear type of legs. This spider almost transparent, its legs wisps of a dancing dark light, like pencil strokes. The legs keep it high off the ground, and there is nothing to it really, just a pale body. An apparition. I saw it walked across our oblong mirror one morning. Then it stopped moving. The mirror looked cracked. I could see my own broken face behind it. Sibaso calls this a post-war spider, a post dream generation spider, a hunger-starvation spider –a political manifestation of death. It is fragile like the membrane around dreams.
When this spider passes by, it looks as though you could blow it off its legs with a whisper directed at its awkwad legs. The joints upon its legs are mere full stops, abbreviations for a death. Its outline a parenthesis. You find this spider in bathtubs in the early hours of the morning, gawky, sliding into corners, its body weaving like thread, shining like muslin, like

malice. It has no predators. It lives off starvation, my uncle says. Who ever would hunt it would have to lick its invisibility off the ground, like spilt salt. It knows how live on a margin, brittle, like a shard of glass. Who would want to est such an already dead thing. In the future there will be no trace of it. It die outside time.

My uncle Sibaso is learning to live without memory, like this spider. He hardly eats. He does not swallow the stars as he used to and takes his rest in the coolness of the house, a pillow held to his belly, a half-finished Coca-cola bottle to his side, its mouth sugary, syrupy, black. He keeps a few crumbs in a plate, to feed his ego, he says. An old coat hangs on the edge of the headboard, dangling royally to the floor like a priest's habit. He searches for a new balm for his wounds. A blue Kariba Battery is on the window sill, recharged by the sun. He has a small portable Panasonic radio which he carries with him and increases the volume whenever he hears something about the war in the Congo. When he learns that this war is over then he will go and join the Zimbabwean army. There are no other jobs available fo someone with his sort of sordid past. There are huge gaps in his memory concerning this country. He spent too many years in the bush.

My uncle is feigning death, as he did in the bush when a dangerous looking spider crept over his arm. He would watch it, holding his breath for as long as he could. He would be still as a rock. There was no mistaking a poisonous spider, all the evidence was there, the legs ferocious, hairypincers. It had a dead weight about it, on your arm. A confident weught. It strolled all over your arm like a deranged dancer. Outrageous in its design and coloration. You could feel it trying to make a decision, wondering if you were human, and if yo were if you were already dead. A spider never wastes its venom. You could feel its belly graze your skin. Poised. It made an art out of inflicting harm and approached you in a daylight. It had a swiftness about it that seemed not to belong to the species. A lithe body. Often it lingered suspiciously. If it moved off quickly then it had granted you a reprieve. The encounter ironic; death near and far. They have a name for this sort of spider in Africa, *umahambemoyeni* –the swimmer in the air. It is 1999, and my uncl Sibaso says he thought he had left this sort of spider in the bush where its charm and dismay belongs. When Ken Saro-Wiwa was hanged seven times before he died my uncle Sibaso tied his own wrists together and lay back on his bed, placing his hands under the pillow. He switched off the radio. He felt that he could not survive the day without injury to himself and was ashamed of the entire continent. He was convinced that he himself deserved to die. On the day he finally turned the radio back on it was reported that a fire in Nigeria had burnt villagers who were collecting oil from a burst pipe. They lay strewn like burnt wood.

My uncle Sibaso did not want to be part of a war which was fought in the open, which consisted of breaking street lights and luminous balconies, drinking house and tailor-shops, fish-seller porches and the smell of roasting plantains. He called this sort of war a window shopping war, an unnecessary war. A war which consisted of ordinary citizens looking for a loaf of bread,and dogs, and roof tops, and tower lights. He did not want the blood-on-tar kind of war where bodies were returned home in bags to be buried by perplexed neighbors. The war of reckless hacking limbs, of bodies burning. He did not want the sunset war witnessed by children and women and invalids. He preferred absence.

He wanted a war in which he waited for days before anything precise happened, while he thought and prepared himself. He wanted to risk his mind, somehow, while lying flat on a rock. He wanted that sort of lizard war, in which he had taken a personal resolve against a personal harm. He did not want a Congo war because he had never been there. How could he fight for a place he had never been. The idea was too absurd for him to tolerate so he waited for the radio to tell him about the rebels who had surrendered. He heard of the revelers in the street, of an Air Zimbabwe flight which was now available to take you to the Congo. It had become some kind of destination, some place where airplanes could land and where tourists and businessmen were encouraged to go. He was already preparing his mind to join the army. He was already in a job. I never listened to the radio directly and only paid attention to what my uncle Sibaso said he had heard.

"... Spider legs", he said, in his new army attire.

Jan-Erik Lundström
Director of BildMuseet, Umeå

Tremor under the still surface, a massive body shouldering black water aside. First a few scattered shapes, unevenly distributed, then areas, sections, regions, then the whole organism, a continent. For a few moments it stands still, rests, as the dark waters sluice off its sides. Then it rapidly reverses, is engulfed by the waters, disappears into the deep... Out of the waters emerges the continent, the grand infinite African continent, the grand infinite continent; into the waters it vanishes...

Thick pre-summer heat and splendid football-madness permeates Barcelona. The Spanish League Championship has been conquered. The entire city is singing, laughing, celebrating. The Rambla de Santa Mónica' glitters in the damp April-evening darkness, restaurants and bars are full to the brim, overflowing onto the streets, the atmosphere is joyous, messy, euphoric. Earlier the same evening, the 'Centre d'Art Santa Mònica' had opened the exhibition *Let there be Light*, a presentation of works by Alfredo Jaar born out of his engagement with the genocide which took place in Rwanda, 1994. Mutualities. Contrasts. An exhibition never to be forgotten.

Having collaborated with Alfredo Jaar on earlier projects, I already had the opportunity to follow his Rwanda-project for some time. The clear insistence on reduction and refinement, the signature gestures of repetition, the act of naming as an act of redemption and celebration, the powerful refusal to represent, the sudden but subtle insertion of micro-narratives and romanticist counterpoints, the corroborated tensions between word and image; all were ingredients in a grandly orchestrated opera that moved towards naming the unnameable, speaking the unspeakable; a sequence of works on the Rwanda tragedy which challenged Adorno by offering dark dense spatial and visual and textual poetry in the face of horror. The Rwanda project had in fact accomplished a remarkable feat, that of organising dignity and forwarding the destiny of individuals, even while addressing a tragedy and human collapse of the magnitude of the Rwandan genocide.

Yet I was completely unprepared that evening when, for the first time, I experienced and witnessed the sculpture "Emergencia". Its impact on me was immediate and overwhelming, like a blow to the solar plexus. I found myself trembling, crying, gasping for breath, stunned, halted. I embraced Jaana, my partner. We were held there fast by the work, standing gazing through many cycles. Might it be possible to describe the experience of "Emergencia" as a confrontation with beauty? Does this work of art fulfil the classical criteria of having arrived at the edge of the sublime? Is it a summation or an exorcism, a requiem or a song of freedom? For "Emergencia" (I was always more comfortable with the Spanish title –which seemed to more clearly maintain its double reference to both *emergency* and ***emergence*** or emerging– than the English "Emergency") is indeed a work where pain and beauty become one and the same, where icon, symbol and allegory are interwoven and fused, where birth and death greet and look each other in the eye.

For this miniature continent seems an incarnation, an embodiment rather than a representation by figurative means; it is a scale model, a topographical map, but simultaneously and more precisely, it is a sculpture, an independent body, an organism, emerging from the oceans. As it rises out of the primal waters, reaches out from the womb, from the grave, the continent is timeless, primordial, bearing all the weight of history on its shoulders, and yet it is, at the same time, exactly and precisely contemporary. And being contemporary, it speaks to its own -as a real continent housing a grand panorama of cultures and peoples– its geopolitical position recognised for an instant as disaster strikes, yet just as swiftly forgotten as the momentum of sensation fades; narrated, depicted in quick drab colours by a media incapable of dealing with nuance. Yet it emerges again, rivers of dark water running off its skin. Again. Then again.

Having thus been struck by "Emergencia" at its premiere in April 1998, I immediately knew that this work of enormous political density had to be shown at the BildMuseet at Umeå University. Straight away, Alfredo Jaar responded positively to the idea. A year later, *Emergencia* had travelled north, across Europe to Sweden, had been rebuilt, reconstructed, and was ready once more to perform its Sisyphean labour. Its home was the Umeå city library, filling a winter garden space, a transparent room that it occupied on its own, surrounded by the library, housed in the midst of literature, knowledge, speech. "Emergencia" calling in the house of knowledge, in turn, reflected in "Emergencia"'s ocean; you walked straight in from the street, and as you searched the shelves for your word, there it is: dark, heavy, enthralling, sharp, heaving out of the water, cleaving into the water. "Emergencia" remained in the library for half a year, through summer and autumn. People travelled from far and wide. New visitors arrived daily, while others came back time and again, spending time with "Emergencia" every day.

Things fall smoothly in place. Alfredo Jaar and I quickly come to realise that neither of us is looking for a traditionally focused catalogue. Surely, "Emergencia" invites dialogue, associations, a discourse of its own; asking questions of Africa, past and future. But just as this work both reflects and grows out of this continent of pain and joy, so we find ourselves summoned to return the conversation and the dialogue to the continent itself.

Hence the idea for this book. Not a catalogue about a work of art called "Emergencia", but rather an invitation to African authors to share their personal views and perspectives on their continent. An open invitation to them to tell, to narrate, to speak their continent at, what was then, the dawning of the new millennium, itself a preliminary and Euro-centric notion of time. This book might just as well be thought of as sculpture, a verbal sculpture, with twenty-five (eighteen in its first edition) singular voices being brought together, observing and shaping their continent, together forming a collective and polyphonic sculpture that maps and moulds its own continental geography.

The book "Emergencia" is consequently not a typical anthology. It does not consist of texts selected and introduced by an editor. While it is true that the authors were selected, the texts they have written, new texts, exclusively for this publication respond to an open, uncircumscribed invitation: contribute words that flow out of your present, from your co-ordinates, physical and mental, on this continent named Africa. What an honour and privilege to be and to have been one of the first readers of these texts.

Neither is the book *Emergencia* to be understood as an overview of African literature. It is not a treatise of literary criticism. But it does include a conscious attempt to be –reasonably– pan-African. In other words, the selection of authors sets out to cover, as far as possible, the geographical variety of the continent. The original texts were conceived in Afrikaans, Arabic, English, French, Portuguese and Spanish (yes, the colonial language map lives on). These texts are now yours.

My sincerest thanks to the authors who have so generously shared their universes with us. I would also like to express my gratitude to Anna Soler-Pont for making her extensive knowledge of African literature available to us, and for co-ordinating contacts with the authors. Thanks once again to SIDA, the Swedish International Development and Co-operation Agency, for their decisive support for the first edition of *Emergencia*, the book, and to ACTAR and MUSAC for the second. For Alfredo: *Un abrazo fuerte* –a warm embrace.

From the water nothing could be known. It kept its secret. Its surface unbroken; a grand mirror reflecting its entire surroundings. Time passes, stillness rules. But then the continent arrives, rises out of the water, Africa the continent, emerges.

Abdourahman Waberi (Somalia)
(Born in 1965). He grew up in Djibouti until he moved to Caen, in Brittany, in 1985, where he now teaches English. He is a novelist, but he has also written several collections of poetry, and usually writes in *Le Monde Diplomatique,* and in some other newspapers. He has been translated into several languages, such as German, English, French, Italian, Spanish and Serbian.

Achmat Dangor (South Africa)
(Born in 1948). Member of the black cultural group Black Thoughts, he was banned for six years from 1973. He has taught South African literature and creative writing at the University of New York and now he is the author of several collections of poetry, a play, short stories and novels. His latest novel, *Kafka's Curse*, has been acclaimed worldwide. He lives in Johannesburg.

Agnès Agboton (Benín)
(Born in 1960). She was born in Porto-Novo but at the age of fifteen she moved to Catalonia (Spain) with her husband. Today, many years after, she is still living in Barcelona as a writer. She is the author of *La cuina africana, Àfrica des dels fogons* and her autobiography *Més enllà del mar de sorra,* published in Catalan and Spanish.

Aly Diallo (Mali)
(Born in 1950). Author of the novels *La revolte du komo,* 2000, *The Failure (The role of the Museum and History in Africa)*, 1986. Vice-minister of Culture and organizer of his countries representatives for the Jazz Festival in New Orleans.

Ama Ata Aidoo (Ghana)
(Born in 1942). She has written poetry, novels, short stories, plays and aslo critical essays. At university, she participated at the Scool of Drama and produced her first two plays when she was still an undergraduate. After graduation, she moved on to the creative writing programme at Stanford University in the USA, and since then she has taught as a research fellow at the Institute of African Studies, University of Ghana. She was Secretary for Education in the military government of Flt. Lt. Jerry Rawlings in the early 1980s.

Aminata Sow Fall (Senegal)
(Born in 1941). Author of five novels, all of them translated into many languages and inspired by the social and political events of her country, Aminata Sow Fall is considered the first published woman novelist from francophone Subsaharian Africa, with her work *Le Revenant* in 1976. She is the owner and director of Éditions Khoudia, an independent publishing house based in Dakar.

Antjie Krog (South Africa)
(Born in 1952). Born in a family of writers. She has published eight volumes of poetry –in Afrikaans– before working as a radio broadcaster during her country's Truth and Reconciliation Commission (TRC), established in 1995 as part of the dismantling of South Africa's racist apartheid laws. She received international recognition for the book she wrote about her TRC experiences, *Country of My Skull: Guilt, Sorrow, and the Limits of Forgiveness in the New South Africa* in 1998, the first book that she wrote in English.

Buchi Emecheta (Nigeria)
(Born in 1944). Moved to England following her husband in 1962. Aged 22, she finally left him and took an honours degree in Sociology while supporting her five children and writing in the early morning. Her novels have been translated into several languages: *In the Ditch, The Joys of Motherhood, Kehinde*...

Calixthe Beyala (Cameroon)
(Born in 1961). After a poor childhood, at the age of seventeen she moved to France. She lived in Malaga for some years, then went on to study Spanish Literature in France. Since 1987 she has not stopped writting, and her novels have been translated abroad, with over one milion copies sold worldwide. She has received the French Academy's *Gran Prix* and the title *Chevalier des Arts et des Lettres.*

Christiane Ramanantsoa (Madagascar)
(Born in 1953). Writer, actress and director. She is also the leader of a theatre company in Antananarivo. Author of the following works: *La fortresse de Zanahary, Tableaux de Madagascar*, both published in 1999.

Donato Ndongo-Bidyogo (Equatorial Guinea)
(Born in 1950). Writer and journalist, he was the director of the Centro Cultural Hispano-Guineano in Malabo and the head of the Spanish news agency Agencia EFE in Central Africa. He is considered the most important representative of hispanic literature in Africa (Ecuatorial Guinea was the only Spanish colony on the continent). He is the author of two novels (*Las tinieblas de tu memoria negra* and *Los poderes de la tempestad*) and several non-fiction books.

Gaston-Paul Effa (Cameroon)
(Born in 1965). Gaston-Paul Effa was born in Cameroon and moved to France at the age of sixteen. He studied Theology and Philosophy at Strasbourg, then in Paris at the Sorbonne. His novels include *Cheval-Roi*; *Le Cri que tu pousses ne réveillera personne*; *Couleurs des Temps*; *Mâ; Tout ce bleu*; which have been translated and published in French and English.

Helen Oyeyemi Olajumoke (Nigeria)
(Born in 1984). From Ibadan she moved to England in 1988 with her mother. Nowadays, she studies Social and Political Sciences in the Corpus Cristi College from Cambridge and also studies International Literature. Her first novel, *The Icarus Girl*, published by Bloomsbury, has already been sold by several international publishers.

Jean-Marie Vianney Rurangwa (Rwanda)
(Born in 1959). After growing up in Burundi, he left for Italy in 1992 and joined the group "Grupo Di Teatro Africano". Author of the plays *Laissez-le vivre, Pour Vous, Femmes!* and the widely acclaimed essays *Le Génocide des Tutsi expliqué à un Étranger* and *Le Figuier.*

José Eduardo Agualusa (Angola)
(Born in 1960). Angolan writer and journalist. Awarded the Portuguese Grand Prize for Literature. He is the author of *Arcadia, The Conspiracy, The Market of the Damned* and *The Rainy Seasons.*

Marlene van Niekerk (South Africa)
(Born in 1954). Poet and novelist, she belongs to a new generation of South African writers who write in Afrikaans. Has published two poetry collections, *Sprokkelster,* 1976, and *Groenstaar,* 1983 and a short story collection, *Die vrou wat haar verkyker vergeet het*, in 1992. Her first novel, *Triomf*, came out in 1994.

Mia Couto (Mozambique)
(Born in 1955) Writer and journalist, in 1988 he was awarded a prize by the Organisation of Mozambican Journalists for his regular columns in *Notícias*, the main newspaper in his country, and in 1991 was awarded the National Prize for Literature in Mozambique. *Terra sonámbula* is his most famous novel, translated into more than ten languages. He lives in Maputo.

Moses Isegawa (Uganda)
(Born in 1963). He qualified as a teacher, and after some years dedicated to teaching History he moved to The Netherlands in 1999 to become a writer, where he now lives. His novels deal with stories about people in Uganda in the 1970's.

Nawal Al-Saadawi (Egypt)
(Born in 1935). Refusing to accept the limitations imposed by both religious and colonial oppresion on most women of rural origin, she qualified as a doctor in 1955 and rose to become Egypt's Director of Public Health. Later in 1980 she was imprisoned under the Sadat regime. Her books have been translated internationally (*Women at point zero, Searching, The Circling Song...*). She lives again in Cairo after many years in the United States.

Nuruddin Farah (Somalia)
(Born in 1945). Author of several novels (*Gifts, Maps, Sardines...*) translated into twelve languages, he is considered one of the most important African intellectuals. Exiled from Somalia since 1972, he lives between Nigeria and England.

Pepetela (Angola)
(Born in 1941). One of Africa's most important writers in Portuguese language. Pepetela was his pseudonym during the Angloan war. He is the author of novels such as *Lueji,* 1997, *Parbola do Cagado Velho,* 1996, *Yaka*, 1996, *A gloriosa familia,* 1991, or *Mayombe,* 1981.

Tierno Monénembo (Guinea)
(Born in 1947). In 1972 he exiled to Senegal, where he started his studies in Natural Sciences. He finished them between Ivory Coast, Algeria and France. He began his literary career in 1979 with *Les crapauds-brousse,* a hard critisim against Sekou Touré's dictatorship. He has also published *Un attiéké pour Elgass, Pelourinho* and *Cinéma*. Today he lives in Normandy.

Véronique Tadjo (Ivory Coast)
(Born in 1955). Author of several novels (*À vol d'oiseau, Champs de bataille et d'amour*), poetry (*Latérite*: Prix ACCT 1984) and of children's books *(Lord of the Dance, Mamy Wata et le monstre:* Prix Unicef 1993). She has been living in many places in Africa and recently moved to South Africa.

Víctor Omgbá (Cameroon)
(Born in 1967). He graduated at the University of Yaoundé, and in 1995 moved to Madrid to continue his studies in Law, which he had begun in Camercon. Some years later, he moved to A Coruña, where he currently lives and works. He works as a journalist for *La Voz de de Galicia* and he regulary participates in the debates of *Radio Voz.* Is the author of the novel *Calella sen saída*, published in Spanish in 2000 by Galaxia Publishers and in Catalan by Galera. He has also written several articles in international magazines.

Yvonne Vera (Zimbabwe)
(Born in 1964). Author of four novels (*Nehanda, Without a Name, Under the Tongue* and *Butterfly Burning*) highly acclaimed and translated into many languages, in Sweden she has been awarded The Voice of Africa 1999. She now works as the director of the National Gallery of Arts in Bulawayo (Zimbabwe).

JUNTA DE CASTILLA Y LEÓN
CULTURE & TOURISM COUNCIL

Councillor
Dña. Silvia Clemente Municio

General Secretary
D. Jesús Ignacio Sesé

General Director of Cultural Promotions and Institutions
D. Alberto Gutiérrez Alberca

FUNDACIÓN SIGLO PARA LAS ARTES DE CASTILLA Y LEÓN

General Director
D. Jesús Mª Gómez Sanz

Visual Arts Director
D. Rafael Doctor Roncero

MUSAC. MUSEO DE ARTE CONTEMPORÁNEO DE CASTILLA Y LEÓN

Director
Rafael Doctor Roncero

Chief Curator
Agustín Pérez Rubio

General Coordinator
Kristine Guzmán

Coordinators
Carlos Ordás
Tania Pardo
Belén Sola

Internships
Araceli Corbo
Mercedes Díaz
Koré Escobar
Marta Gerveno
Clara Merín
Raúl Ordás
María Soria
Blanca de la Torre

PUBLICATION

Published by
MUSAC
ACTAR

Editorial Coordination
Alfredo Jaar
MUSAC
Pontas Literary & Film Agency

Translations
BabelTraductors

Graphic Design
Ramon Prat

Printing
Ingoprint SA

Paper
Century Cotton Wove,
Premium White 120 grs
Distributed by COYDIS
Explanada, 8, 2° A 28040 MADRID
Tel. +34 915 360 688

Distribution
ACTAR
Roca i Batlle 2-4. 08023 Barcelona
Tel +34 93 418 7759 Fax +34 93 418 6707
info@actar-mail.com

ISBN 84-932325-6-4 (MUSAC)
ISBN 84-95951-90-8 (ACTAR)
DL B-13.183-05

Printed and bound in the European Union

Fundación Siglo
para las Artes de Castilla y León

MUSEO DE ARTE CONTEMPORÁNEO
DE CASTILLA Y LEÓN